GENERAL INFORMATION FOR
GRAIN LOADING

INCLUDING

U.S. Coast Guard
Regulations For
Bulk Grain Cargoes

AND

Chapter VI of
The International
Conventions For
The Safety of
Life at Sea

(1948 and 1960)

NATIONAL CARGO BUREAU, INC. 99 JOHN STREET • NEW YORK 38, N. Y.

UNITED STATES COAST GUARD

ADDRESS REPLY TO:
COMMANDANT
U.S. COAST GUARD
HEADQUARTERS
WASHINGTON 25, D.C.

This booklet, which has been prepared and printed by the National Cargo Bureau, Inc., fulfills a need for supplying guidance information to shipowners, ship operators, agents, masters, and others relative to the handling of bulk grain.

Subject to the understanding that the information contained therein relative to the grain loading arrangements and stability of various typical vessel design types shall not be used as a substitute for the specific vessel information called for by 144.20-34 and 144.20-36 of CG-266, Rules and Regulations For Bulk Grain Cargoes as well as by 93.10 of CG-257, Rules and Regulations For Cargo and Miscellaneous Vessels, the Coast Guard endorses this publication.

D. McG. MORRISON
Vice Admiral, U. S. Coast Guard
Acting Commandant

CONTENTS

PREFACE

This booklet contains a compilation of Bulk Grain Regulations, recommendations, suggestions and other information relating to loading of bulk grain aboard vessels and is intended as a handy reference for surveyors and members of the Maritime Industry.

The information in the booklet is based upon compliance with CG-266, U. S. Coast Guard Rules and Regulations for Bulk Grain Cargoes, which in turn reflects the extent of the United States' acceptance of the provisions of Chapter VI of the Safety of Life at Sea Convention, 1960 as equivalent to Chapter VI of the Safety of Life at Sea Convention, 1948. The information herein does not necessarily conform in all particulars to the conditions under which other countries may accept the related provisions of Chapter VI of the 1960 SOLAS Convention as equivalent to the provisions of Chapter VI of the 1948 SOLAS Convention.

Since the 1948 Safety of Life at Sea Convention is still in effect, the acceptance of loading arrangements based upon the 1960 Convention should, in the case of foreign vessels, be limited only to vessels belonging to countries which are parties to the 1948 SOLAS Convention and which additionally have formally accepted the 1960 SOLAS Convention as equivalent thereto with respect to grain stowage requirements. In the case of such foreign vessels, the specific vessels concerned are required to be provided with the stability and grain loading information prescribed by the 1960 Convention and approved by the country of registry. All foreign vessels not meeting these conditions should be required to be loaded in compliance with Chapter VI of the 1948 Convention.

The diagrams adjacent to the related portions of the Coast Guard Rules contained herein are not a part thereof but have been added by the National Cargo Bureau for illustrative purposes.

This booklet has been prepared from information obtained from sources believed to be reliable and accurate. National Cargo Bureau does not guarantee its accuracy and completeness and does not assume any responsibility or liability for damage which may arise from the use of this booklet or its contents.

*This Booklet Supersedes Former Booklet
Issued by National Cargo Bureau in 1957.*

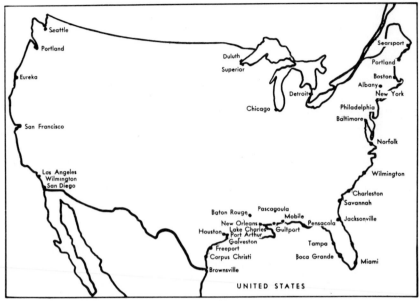

LOCATIONS OF NATIONAL CARGO BUREAU, INC. OFFICES

The following ports are served through the offices indicated:

ATLANTIC COAST
Providence, R. I. (Boston)
New London, Conn. (Boston)
New Haven, Conn. (New York)
Bridgeport, Conn. (New York)
Richmond, Va. (Norfolk)
Newport News, Va. (Norfolk)
Morehead City, N. C. (Wilmington)
Georgetown, S. C. (Charleston)
Brunswick, Ga. (Savannah)
Kings Bay, Fla. (Jacksonville)
Fernandina, Fa. (Jacksonville)
Cape Canaveral, Fla. (Jacksonville)
Port Everglades, Fla. (Miami)

GULF COAST
Beaumont, Tex. (Port Arthur)
Port Isabel, Tex. (Brownsville)
Panama City, Fla. (Pensacola)

GREAT LAKES
Superior, Wisc. (Duluth)
Green Bay, Wisc. (Chicago)
Milwaukee, Wisc. (Chicago)
Kenosha, Wisc. (Chicago)
Saginaw, Mich. (Chicago and Detroit)
Muskegon, Mich. (Chicago and Detroit)
Holland, Mich. (Chicago and Detroit)
Toledo, Ohio (Chicago and Detroit)
Cleveland, Ohio (Chicago and Detroit)
Ashtabula, Ohio (Chicago and Detroit)
Buffalo, N. Y. (Chicago and Detroit)
Oswego, N. Y. (Chicago and Detroit)

PACIFIC COAST
Tacoma, Wash. (Seattle)
Aberdeen, Wash. (Seattle)
Grays Harbor, Wash. (Seattle)
Willapa Harbor, Wash. (Seattle)
Astoria, Ore. (Portland)
Newport, Ore. (Portland)
Coos Bay, Ore. (Portland)
Stockton, Calif. (San Francisco)
Port Hueneme, Calif. (Los Angeles)

NATIONAL CARGO BUREAU, INC.

National Cargo Bureau was incorporated as a non-profit organization in May 1952 and began its actual operation on November 19, 1952. The Bureau was created to render assistance to the United States Coast Guard in discharging its responsibilities under the 1948 International Convention for Safety of Life at Sea* and for other purposes closely related thereto.

By assignment and under the authority of the United States Coast Guard, the certificates issued by National Cargo Bureau, Inc. may be accepted as prima facie evidence of compliance with the provisions of the Dangerous Cargo Act and the Rules and Regulations for Bulk Grain Cargo.

National Cargo Bureau, Inc. is a relatively new name but in effect it is a continuation and amplification on a broader base of the inspection services formerly performed by The Board of Underwriters of New York and The Board of Marine Underwriters of San Francisco and now operates on a nation-wide basis.

*To be superseded by the 1960 Safety of Life at Sea Convention when ratified.

CONTROL SHEET FOR CHANGES

Federal Register date	Section No.	Subject

THE TERMINOLOGY FOR NUMBERING

This is an explanation of the numbering system used in Coast Guard pamphlets containing regulations and is the same as that used in the Code of Federal Regulations.

The rules and regulations in regard to merchant vessel inspection are divided into chapters, subchapters, parts, subparts, sections, paragraphs, subparagraphs, and subdivisions. The chapters are numbered with a Roman numeral and the subchapters are given alphabetical designations. The part in this pamphlet is numbered 144. The terminology for numbering may be described as follows:

Terminology	Example
Part	144
Subpart	144.01
Section	144.01–1
Paragraph	144.01–1 (a)
Subparagraph	144.01–1 (a) (1)
Subdivision	144.01–1 (a) (1) (i)

PART 144 — LOADING AND STOWAGE OF GRAIN CARGOES

144.01 PREFACE

144.01–1 Purpose

144.01–1 (a) The purpose of the regulations in this subchapter is to promote safety in the handling, stowage, and transportation of grain on board vessels within the limits of the jurisdiction of the United States, including its territories and possessions, excepting only the Panama Canal Zone, and to make more effective the provisions of the International Convention for the Safety of Life at Sea, 1948, relative to the carriage of grain.

144.10   GENERAL REQUIREMENTS

144.10–1   Scope

144.10–1(a) The regulations in this part contain the minimum requirements for the handling, stowage, and transportation of loose grain in bulk on board vessels.

144.10–10   Application to vessels

144.10–10(a) The regulations in this part apply to every passenger vessel and every cargo vessel of 500 gross tons or over loading loose grain in bulk within the limits defined in Paragraph 144.01–1(a) for an international voyage (excepting on the Great Lakes).

144.10–10(b) The regulations in this part apply to every United States passenger vessel and every United States cargo vessel of 500 gross tons or over carrying loose grain in bulk as cargo on an international voyage (excepting on the Great Lakes).

144.10–20   Definitions

144.10–20(a) For the purpose of the regulations in this part the definitions in this section shall apply.

144.10–20(b) "Grain" shall include wheat, maize (corn), oats, rye, barley, rice, pulses, and seeds.

144.10–20(c) "Light grain" means oats, light barley or cottonseed.

144.10–20(d) "Light barley" means barley which weighs:

144.10–20(d)(1) 50 pounds or under per full bushel of 1.2445 cubic feet (U.S.A.); or,

144.10–20(d)(2) 51.575 pounds or under per full bushel of 1.2837 cubic feet (U.K.).

144.10–20(e) "Heavy grain" means all grain other than oats, light barley, or cottonseed.

144.10–20(f) "Bin" means a section of the cargo space in the tween decks or superstructure completely enclosed on all sides.

144.10–25   Certification by National Cargo Bureau, Inc.

144.10–25(a) Certificates of loading of the National Cargo Bureau, Inc. may be accepted as prima facie evidence of compliance with the requirements in this subchapter.

144.10–30   Shifting boards

144.10–30(a) Shifting boards shall be of good sound timber of minimum thickness of 2 inches, and fitted grain tight.

144.10–30(b) The maximum unsupported span to be allowed

for shifting boards of various thicknesses shall be as set forth in Table 144.10–30 (b).

Table 144.10–30 (b)

Thickness	Span	Housing of bulkhead
		Inches
2-inch planks	Unsupported span not to exceed 8 feet	3
2½-inch planks	Unsupported span not to exceed 11 feet	3
3-inch planks	Unsupported span not to exceed 13 feet	3

144.10–30 (c) Shifting boards shall be securely housed at bulkheads, and where permanent angle bars are not available for this purpose, wood cants shall be fitted not less than 6 inches in width and 3 inches in thickness and suitably shored.

144.10–30 (d) Where 2½-inch or 3-inch shifting boards are used the boards may be butt-jointed in way of the uprights and at least 4 inches of plank shall be supported. Where 2 inch shifting boards are used the joints shall overlap by at least 9 inches in way of the uprights.

144.10–30 (e) Where no special arrangements are made for grain tight filling between the beams, wood filling pieces of the same thickness as the shifting boards shall be fitted grain tight between the beams, and shall be secured in place by cleats or scabs at both ends and fitted both sides. The cleats or scabs shall be at least 2 inches by 4 inches and shall extend the full depth of the filling piece and to an equal distance thereunder, and shall be securely spiked or bolted to the shifting boards and filling pieces.

144.10–40 Uprights

144.10–40 (a) Uprights shall be of wood or steel.

144.10–40 (b) Wood uprights shall not be less than 10 inches in width and 2 inches in thickness.

144.10–40 (c) Uprights shall be cleated to the tank top or ceiling where fitted, and when an upright is not securely housed at the top the uppermost supporting shores or stay shall be not more than 18 inches below the deck or top of the upright.

144.10–40 (d) (1) Where a tier of closely spaced pillars in a hold or compartment is utilized for supporting the shifting boards at the middle line, the sizes of the pillars shall be in accordance with the rules of approved classification societies for deck beam pillars.

144.10–40 (d) (2) Where the pillars are not reeled or staggered, additional support shall be provided by means of hook-bolts and vertical tie plates or uprights secured to the pillars.

8

Such tie plates shall consist of plates not less than 3 inches in width and ½-inch in thickness and shall be through-bolted at intervals of not more than 3 feet.

144.10–40 (e) The horizontal distances between the centers of uprights shall be specified in Paragraph 144.10–30 (b). Wood uprights used in association with wire stays, spaced as in Section 144.10–60, shall be not less than 11 inches in width and 3 inches in thickness.

144.10–40 (f) The construction and dimensions of angle bar uprights used in association with wire stays shall conform to, or be equivalent to, the following:

144.10–40 (f) (1) *Type I.* Each upright shall consist of 4 angle bars 4 by 4 by 0.40 inches and steel plate 11½ inches wide by 0.50 inch thick riveted to form one complete structure allowing 4-inch housings on both forward and after sides. Equivalent brackets riveted to head and heel shall be fitted, each to take five ⅞-inch bolts with corresponding lugs and/or angles on tank top, tunnel top, and hatch webs. See Figure 144.10–40 (f) (1) for illustration.

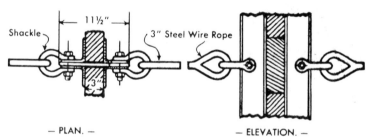

— PLAN. —   — ELEVATION. —

FIGURE 144.10–40 (f) (1).

144.10–40 (f) (2) *Type II.* Metal uprights in accordance with Table 144.10–40 (f) (2). Vertical angle bars shall be connected at head and heel to the tank top, tunnel top, deck beams, and hatch webs by angle lugs having two ⅞-inch bolts in each angle bar upright and equivalent fastenings to tank top, tunnel top, deck beams, and hatch webs. The vertical angle bars shall be bolted together through the shifting boards by ⅞-inch bolts not more than 4 feet apart. See Figure 144.10–40 (f) (2) for illustration with overlap of shifting boards.

9

Table 144.10–40 (f) (2)

Horizontal distance between centers of uprights	Vertical spans supported by each stay Feet	Sizes of angle bars Inches
8′ (2″ shifting boards)	8	3 x 3 x 0.38
8′ (2″ shifting boards)	11	3½ x 3½ x 0.38
8′ (2″ shifting boards)	14	4½ x 3½ x 0.44
11′ (2½″ shifting boards)	8	3 x 3 x 0.38
11′ (2½″ shifting boards)	11	4 x 3½ x 0.40
11′ (2½″ shifting boards)	14	6 x 3½ x 0.40
13′ (3″ shifting boards)	8	3 x 3 x 0.38
13′ (3″ shifting boards)	11	4 x 3½ x 0.42
13′ (3″ shifting boards)	14	6 x 3½ x 0.40

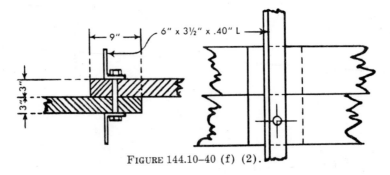

FIGURE 144.10–40 (f) (2).

144.10–40 (g) Wood uprights shall be supported by steel wire rope stays set up at the ship's side, or by wood shores securely heeled against the permanent structure of the ship, or by other approved means.

144.10–50 Shores

144.10–50 (a) All wood shores shall be of good sound timber in a single piece. Spliced shores shall not be used.

144.10–50 (b) The vertical spacing of wood shores shall be as follows:

144.10–50 (b) (1) Except as provided in Paragraph 144.10–40 (c), the uppermost shore shall be not more than 7 feet below the top of the upright and succeeding shores shall be spaced 7 feet apart measured vertically from the uppermost shore downwards, except that a distance of 8 feet may be allowed between the lowest shore and the heel support.

144.10–50 (b) (2) Shores may be heeled on the tanktop or ceiling provided the heels are secured by cleats or cants and efficiently braced against the permanent structure.

144.10–50 (b) (3)   Shores shall not be heeled directly against the ship's side plating.

144.10–50 (c)   The sizes of wood shores shall be set forth in Table 144.10–50 (c).

Table 144.10–50 (c)

Length of shores	Minimum sizes	
	Rectangular section *Inches*	Circular section diameter *Inches*
Not exceeding 16 feet	4 x 6	5½
Over 16 feet and not exceeding 20 feet	6 x 6	7
Over 20 feet and not exceeding 24 feet	6 x 8	7½
Over 24 feet and not exceeding 28 feet	¹ 6 x 8	8
Over 28 feet	¹ 6 x 8	8½

¹ Securely bridged at about midlength.

144.10–50 (d). Where the spacings of the shores or uprights are less than those prescribed by Paragraphs 144.10–30 (b) and 144.10–50 (b), the sizes of the shores may be reduced in proportion, and where, in special circumstances, the spacings of the shores or uprights are increased, additional strength shall be provided as may be prescribed by the District Commander of the United States Coast Guard or his authorized representative.

144.10–50 (e)   Shores should normally be fitted at an angle not exceeding 10 degrees from the horizontal; where this angle is exceeded the next larger size of shore to that required by its length shall be used. The angle between any shore and the surface to be supported shall not exceed 45 degrees from the horizontal.

144.10–60   Stays

144.10–60 (a)   Where uprights are secured as approved at both head and heel, one stay on each side of each upright will be accepted in holds 20 feet and under in depth, to be placed at approximately ⅓ of the distance below the deck. Where the hold is more than 20 feet deep, 2 stays on each side of each upright shall be required, the upper stays to be placed at approximately ¼ of the distance below the deck and the lower stays at half the depth of the hold. Depths shall be measured to top of floor, inner bottom or tunnel top.

144.10–60 (b)   Where wire stays are used the following provisions shall apply:

144.10–60 (b) (1)   The stays shall be of at least 3-inch circumference flexible steel wire rope and shall be fitted horizontally;

144.10–60 (b) (2) The rigging screws shall be at least 1¼-inch diameter and shall be fitted in accessible positions;

144.10–60 (b) (3) The shackles shall be at least 1 inch;

144.10–60 (b) (4) The eye bolts through the wood or angle bar uprights shall be at least 1¼ inches;

144.10–60 (b) (5) At least ⅞-inch screw bolts and nuts shall be provided as may be necessary for securing the wood uprights or steel angle bars;

144.10–60 (b) (6) Eye plates of at least 1 inch thickness shall be securely riveted to the side stringers or frames, or at least 1 inch shackles passed through the frames.

144.10–60 (c) Where in accordance with Section 144.20–20 shifting boards do not extend the full depth of the hold, the shifting boards and their uprights shall be supported or stayed as provided for in the regulations in this part or to the satisfaction of the District Commander of the United States Coast Guard or his authorized representative.

144.10–70 Feeders, bins, and bulkheads

144.10–70 (a) Feeders, bins, and bulkheads shall be of sufficient strength to withstand the pressure of the head of grain contained therein and shall be made grain tight. When the height of the tween decks is greater than normal, special attention should be given to the stiffening and support of feeders and bins.

144.10–70 (b) Wood feeders and bin bulkheads may be constructed:

144.10–70 (b) (1) Of planks worked vertically not less than 2½-inch thickness, but where the vertical unsupported span exceeds 8 feet the thickness of the planks shall be increased, or additional stiffening fitted; or,

144.10–70 (b) (2) Of studding and lined with grain tight boards 2 inches in thickness or two 1 inch layers of shiplap, laid horizontally with broken joints. Studding where possible shall be placed inside the hatch coamings and shall be not less than 4 inches by 6 inches on edge spaced not more than 2 feet centers.

144.10–70 (c) Wing feeders may be constructed in a similar manner around trimming hatches. In all cases the planks at the corners shall be well secured to substantial vertical cants.

144.10–70 (d) Where the depth of the hatch end beams or coamings exceeds 15 inches below the surface of the deck, feeding holes shall be provided to allow the grain to flow through the coamings into the hold or tween decks; where the depth of the coamings below the surface of the deck exceeds 15 inches and is not more than 18 inches feeding holes 2 inches in diameter shall be provided. Where the depth exceeds 18 inches feeding holes of 3½-inch diameter shall be provided. Feeding holes shall be spaced approximately 2 feet apart.

144.10–70(e) Engine room, boiler room, stokehold bulkheads and donkey boiler recesses where subjected to heat shall be sheathed with wood and made grain tight. An air space of at least 6 inches shall be left between the bulkhead and the sheathing and a box trunk ventilator 6 inches by 8 inches shall be provided from the top of the air space to a ventilator or hatchway, or other equal and approved means of ventilation adopted. Sheathing shall be supported on vertical runners spaced not more than 2 feet centers and shall consist of 2 inch planks or two thicknesses of 1 inch boards laid to break joint. Other approved means of insulation may be accepted.

144.10–70(f) Feeders or bin bulkheads may be constructed of bagged grain: *Provided,* That:

144.10–70(f)(1) The bags are tightly stowed and interlocked.

144.10–70(f)(2) Whenever practicable the bags are so stowed as to engage firmly with the vessel's sides, bulkheads, and other convenient structures. Where this is not possible, the bagged bulkheads are to be not less than 11 feet (mean) in thickness and stepped.

144.10–70(f)(3) Transverse bagged bulkheads not in way of hatchways or forming feeders but supporting grain on one side only are to be not less than 11 feet (mean) in thickness and stepped.

144.10–70(f)(4) In place of bagged grain, as required by this section, cased, baled, or other suitable cargo may be used provided it is equally strongly supported and made grain tight with strong separation cloths.

KEY TO DIAGRAMS

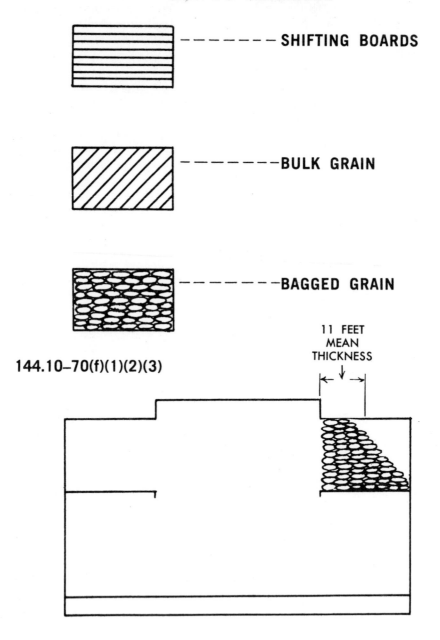

SHIFTING BOARDS

BULK GRAIN

BAGGED GRAIN

11 FEET
MEAN
THICKNESS

144.10–70(f)(1)(2)(3)

144.10–80   Security of hatches

144.10–80(a)   Vessels carrying loose grain in bulk shall have suitable means of securing hatchways and other weather deck openings. Hatch covers and their supports shall be in good condition and properly battened down using good and sufficient tarpaulins, cleats and wedges where necessary.

144.10–90   Equivalents

144.10–90(a)   Where the regulations in this part require a particular fitting, appliance or apparatus or type thereof, shall be fitted or carried in a ship, or that any particular provisions shall be made, the District Commander of the United States Coast Guard or his authorized representative may allow any other fitting, appliances or apparatus, or type thereof, to be fitted or carried, or any other provision to be made, if it is satisfactorily shown that such other fitting, appliance or apparatus, or type thereof, or provision is at least as effective as that required by the regulations in this part.

144.10–90(b)   In any case where it is shown to the satisfaction of the Commandant that the use of specified loading and stowage requirements in this part are unreasonable or impracticable, the Commandant may permit the use of equivalent loading and stowage requirements in lieu of those described in this part to such extent and upon such conditions as will insure to his satisfaction a degree of safety consistent with the minimum standards set forth in Subparts 144.10 to 144.30, inclusive.

144.10–95   Responsibility of owner or master

144.10–95(a)   The loading of bulk grain in accordance with the regulations in this part is a responsibility of the master, who shall designate a competent responsible person to be in constant attendance during loading operations. Nothing in the regulations in this part shall be deemed to relieve the owner or master of a ship from taking all necessary and reasonable precautions to prevent grain from shifting.

144.20   DETAILED LOADING AND STOWAGE REQUIREMENTS

144.20–1   Trimming and filling

144.20–1(a)   The safe loading of grain, in accordance with the regulations in this part, is vitally dependent upon compartments which are treated as entirely filled, being actually well trimmed so as to fill all the spaces between the beams and in the wings and ends. It is equally important that the feeders be loaded and trimmed so as to contain at least the minimum percentage of grain required by the regulations in this part.

144.20–1(b)   Spaces which are to be partly filled and bagged

15

off, or equivalent, must be levelled for proper bagging.

144.20–2   Bagged grain

144.20–2(a) Bagged grain stowed in a hold, compartment or bin with loose grain in bulk shall be in sound bags, well filled and securely closed.

144.20–10   Stowage of full holds and compartments

144.20–10(a) Subject to the provisions of Section 144.20–22, any hold or compartment which is entirely filled with bulk grain shall be divided either by a longitudinal bulkhead or by a shifting board in line with, or not more than 5 percent of the molded breadth of the vessel from the centerline; or by longitudinal bulkheads or shifting boards off the centerline of the vessel, port and starboard, provided the distance between them shall not exceed 60 percent of the molded breadth of the vessel, and that in this latter case trimming hatches of suitable size shall be provided in the wings at longitudinal intervals of not more than 25 feet with end trimming hatches placed not more than 12 feet from transverse bulkheads. In every case the longitudinal bulkheads or shifting boards shall be properly constructed and fitted grain tight with proper fillings between the beams. In holds such longitudinal bulkheads or shifting boards shall extend downwards from the underside of the deck to a distance of at least one-third of the depth of the hold or 8 feet, whichever is the greater. In compartments in tween decks and superstructures they shall extend from deck to deck. Except as provided otherwise in this section, longitudinal bulkheads or shifting boards shall extend to the top of the feeders of the hold or compartment in which they are situated.

144.20-10(a)

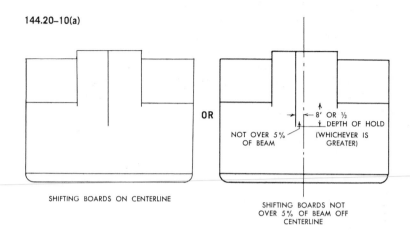

OR

NOT OVER 5%
OF BEAM

8' OR ⅓
DEPTH OF HOLD
(WHICHEVER IS
GREATER)

SHIFTING BOARDS ON CENTERLINE

SHIFTING BOARDS NOT
OVER 5% OF BEAM OFF
CENTERLINE

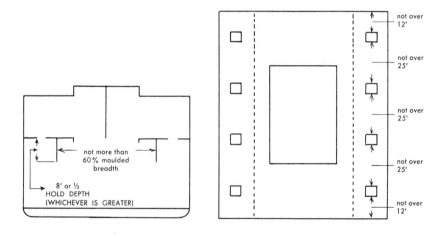

not more than
60% moulded
breadth

8' or ⅓
HOLD DEPTH
(WHICHEVER IS GREATER)

not over
12'

not over
25'

not over
25'

not over
25'

not over
12'

17

144.20–10 (b) In the case of vessels loaded with bulk grain other than linseed, in which a metacentric height (after correction for the free surface effects of liquids in tanks and as otherwise noted in this part) is maintained throughout the voyage of not less than 1¾ percent of the vessel's beam but not less than 12 inches in the case of one or two deck vessels, and not less than 2 percent of the vessel's beam but not less than 14 inches in the case of other vessels, longitudinal bulkheads or shifting boards need not be fitted in the following locations and subject to the following conditions:

144.20–10 (b) (1) Below and within 7 feet of a feeder, but only in way of a hatchway, if that feeder contains, or all the feeders collectively feeding a compartment contain, not less than 5 percent of the quantity of grain carried in that compartment.

144.20–10 (b) (2) In feeders which meet the requirements of subparagraph (1) of this paragraph and which have such dimensions that the free grain surface will remain within the feeders throughout the voyage, after allowing for a settling of grain amounting to 2 percent of the volume of the compartment fed and a shift of the free grain surface to an angle of 12 degrees to the horizontal. In calculating the net minimum metacentric height, the heeling moment due to such a grain shift shall be allowed for by taking a deduction equal to this moment divided by the product of the displacement and the sine of 5 degrees.

144.20–10(b)(1)(2)

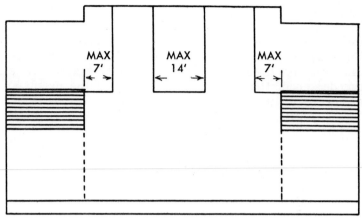

NOTE: 1. REQUIRES STIPULATED STABILITY
2. ONLY FOR GRAIN OTHER
   THAN LINSEED

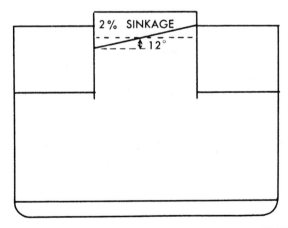

$$\text{DEDUCTION TO GM} = \frac{\text{FEEDER LENGTH} \times (\text{FEEDER BREADTH})^3}{5 \times \text{STOWAGE FACTOR} \times \text{DISPLACEMENT}}$$

NOTE: ONLY FOR GRAIN OTHER
   THAN LINSEED

144.20–10 (b) (3) In way of the hatchway where the bulk grain beneath the hatchway is trimmed in the form of a saucer hard up to the deckhead beyond the hatchway and is topped off with bagged grain or other suitable bagged cargo extending to a height in the center of the saucer of not less than 6 feet above the top of the bulk grain (measured below the deck line). In this case, the bagged grain or other suitable bagged cargo shall fill the hatchway and the saucer below and shall be stowed tightly against the deckhead, the longitudinal bulkheads, the hatchway beams and the hatchway side and end coamings. For the purposes of this subparagraph suitable packaged general cargo having a stowage factor of not less than 25 cubic feet or not more than 70 cubic feet per ton, and of such' unit dimension that it can be stowed tightly to completely fill the saucer, may be used in place of bagged cargo provided a tarpaulin or separation cloth is used between the cargo and the grain.

144.20–20   Feeders required

144.20–20 (a) Except as otherwise provided in Subparagraph 144.20–10 (b) (3) and as subsequently otherwise provided in this section, any hold or compartment which is entirely filled with bulk grain shall be fed by suitably placed and properly constructed feeders so as to secure a free flow of grain from the feeder to all parts of that hold or compartment. Each feeder shall contain not less than $2\frac{1}{2}$ percent nor more than 8 percent of the quantity of grain carried in that part of the hold or compartment that it feeds, except as provided in Subparagraph 144.20–10 (b) (1). Feeders which do not extend to the weather deck but which instead open up into a tween deck shall either be of such dimensions and filling level that a shift of grain free surface to an angle of 12 degrees to the horizontal cannot spill out of the feeder, or the grain free surface shall be secured against such shifting and spillage.

144.20–20 (b) When bulk grain is carried in deep tanks primarily constructed for the carriage of liquids, or in other spaces of comparable size, location, arrangement, and construction, of breadth not exceeding half the vessel's beam, or that are divided by one or more permanent steel longitudinal divisions fitted grain tight, feeders to these spaces may be omitted if the tanks and tank hatchways are completely filled and the hatch covers secured.

144.20–10(b)(3)

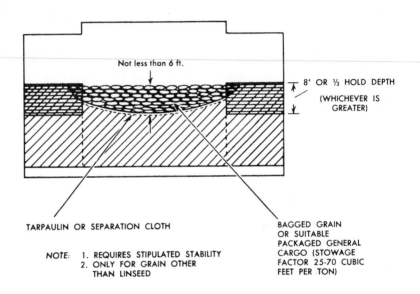

Not less than 6 ft.

8' OR 1/3 HOLD DEPTH
(WHICHEVER IS
GREATER)

TARPAULIN OR SEPARATION CLOTH

BAGGED GRAIN
OR SUITABLE
PACKAGED GENERAL
CARGO (STOWAGE
FACTOR 25-70 CUBIC
FEET PER TON)

NOTE: 1. REQUIRES STIPULATED STABILITY
2. ONLY FOR GRAIN OTHER
THAN LINSEED

144.20–22   Stowage of partly filled holds and compartments

144.20–22 (a) Subject to the provisions of Section 144.20–24, if any hold or compartment is partly filled with bulk grain, it shall comply with both of the following conditions:

144.20–22 (a) (1) It shall be divided by a longitudinal bulkhead or shifting boards, in line with, or not more than 5 percent of the molded breadth of the vessel from the centerline or by longitudinal bulkheads or shifting boards off the centerline of the vessel port and starboard, provided that the distance between them shall not exceed 60 percent of the molded breadth of the vessel. In every case the longitudinal bulkheads or shifting boards shall be properly constructed and shall extend from the bottom of the deck, as the case may be, to a height of not less than 2 feet above the surface of the bulk grain. In the case of vessels loaded with bulk grain other than linseed, in which a metacentric height (after correction for the free surface effects of liquids in tanks) is maintained throughout the voyage of not less than 1¾ percent of the vessel's beam but not less than 12 inches in the case of one or two deck vessels, and not less than 2 percent of the vessel's beam but not less than 14 inches in the case of other vessels, longitudinal bulkheads or shifting boards may be omitted in way of the hatchway.

144.20–22 (a)(1)

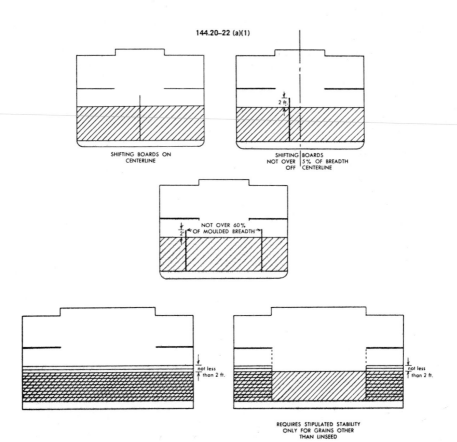

SHIFTING BOARDS ON
CENTERLINE

SHIFTING BOARDS
NOT OVER 5% OF BREADTH
OFF CENTERLINE

NOT OVER 60%
OF MOULDED BREADTH

not less
than 2 ft.

not less
than 2 ft.

REQUIRES STIPULATED STABILITY
ONLY FOR GRAINS OTHER
THAN LINSEED

NOTE: SEE 144.20-22(a) (2) FOR SECURING WITH BAGGED GRAIN
OR OTHER SUITABLE CARGO

144.20–22(a)(2) The bulk grain shall be levelled and topped off with bagged grain or other suitable cargo tightly stowed and extending to a height of not less than 4 feet above the top of the bulk grain within spaces or portions of spaces divided by such longitudinal bulkheads or shifting boards, and not less than 5 feet within portions of spaces not so divided. The bagged grain or other suitable cargo shall be supported on suitable platforms laid over the whole surface of the bulk grain. Such platforms shall consist of bearers spaced not more than 4 feet apart and 1 inch boards laid thereon spaced not more than 4 inches apart, or of strong separation cloths with adequate overlapping.

144.20–22(b) Unless stability data indicates that the metacentric height maintained throughout the voyage (after correction for the free surface effects of liquids in tanks) is at least 1¾ percent of the vessel's beam but not less than 12 inches in the case of one or two deck vessels, and not less than 2 percent of the vessel's beam but not less than 14 inches in the case of other vessels, not more than two holds or compartments shall be partly filled with bulk grain; except that other holds or compartments may be partly filled with bulk grain if they are filled up to the deckhead with bagged or other suitable cargo. For the purpose of this paragraph the following conditions apply:

144.20–22(b)(1) Superimposed tween decks shall be regarded as separate compartments and separate from any lower hold below them.

144.20–22(b)(2) Feeders and partly filled spaces, referred to in Subparagraph 144.20–30(a)(2) shall not be regarded as compartments.

144.20–22(b)(3) Holds or compartments provided with one or more grain tight longitudinal divisions shall be regarded as one hold or compartment.

144.20–22 (a)(2)

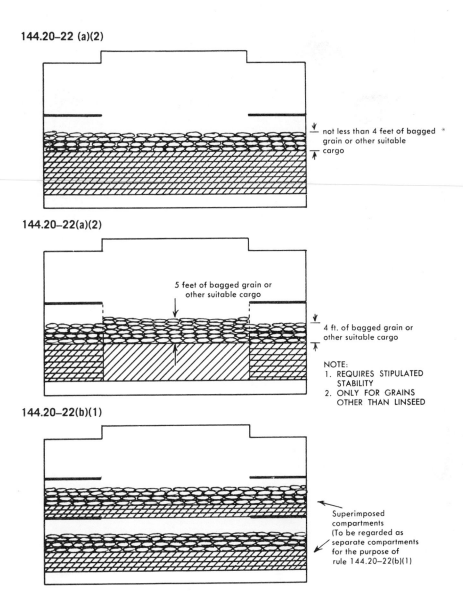

not less than 4 feet of bagged grain or other suitable cargo

144.20–22(a)(2)

5 feet of bagged grain or other suitable cargo

4 ft. of bagged grain or other suitable cargo

NOTE:
1. REQUIRES STIPULATED STABILITY
2. ONLY FOR GRAINS OTHER THAN LINSEED

144.20–22(b)(1)

Superimposed compartments (To be regarded as separate compartments for the purpose of rule 144.20–22(b)(1)

144.20–24 Exceptions to the requirements for longitudinal bulkheads

144.20–24(a) The fitting of longitudinal bulkheads or shifting boards in accordance with the provisions of Section 144.20–10 and Section 144.20–22 is not required under the following conditions:

144.20–24(a)(1) In a lower hold (which term also includes the lower part of the hold of a single deck vessel) if the bulk grain therein does not exceed one-third of the capacity of the hold, or where such lower hold is divided by a shaft tunnel, one-half the capacity of that lower hold; or,

144.20–24(a)(2) In any space in a tween deck or superstructure provided that the wings are tightly stowed with bagged grain or other suitable cargo to a breadth on each side of not less than 20 percent of the breadth of the vessel in way thereof; or,

144.20–24(a)(3) In those parts of spaces where the maximum breadth of the deckhead within the said spaces does not exceed one-half of the molded breadth of the vessel.

144.20–24 (a)(1)

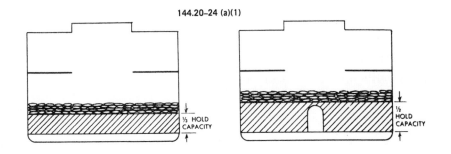

144.20–24 (a)(2)

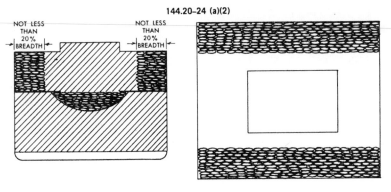

144.20–24 (a)(3)

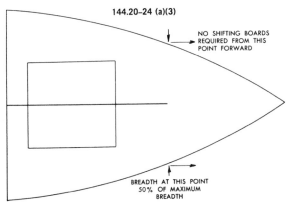

144.20–26 Trimming and bagging of end spaces

144.20–26 (a) When the distance, measured in a fore and aft line, from any part of a hold or compartment to the nearest feeder exceeds 25 feet, the bulk grain in the end spaces beyond 25 feet from the nearest feeder shall be levelled off at a depth of at least 6 feet below the deck, and the end spaces filled with bagged grain built up on a suitable platform constructed as required in Subparagraph 144.20–22 (a) (2).

144.20–26(a)

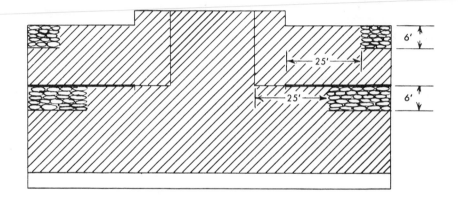

144.20–28 Common loading

144.20–28 (a) For the purpose of Section 144.20–10 and Section 144.20–20 lower holds and tween deck spaces over them may be loaded as one compartment under the following conditions:

144.20–28 (a) (1) The hatches to spaces so treated as common spaces shall be of such proportions and shall have sufficient volume within their coamings and above deck so as to serve as feeders, based upon the total volume of the common spaces served.

144.20–28 (a) (2) Longitudinal bulkheads or shifting boards shall be fitted deck to deck, and in all cases for the full length of the space, in the tween deck of a vessel having two decks; in all other cases the longitudinal bulkheads or shifting boards shall be fitted for the upper third of the total depth of the common spaces.

144.20–28 (a) (3) In order to secure an adequate flow of grain all spaces shall comply with the requirements of Section 144.20–26. Additionally, openings shall be provided in the wings of the deck immediately below the uppermost deck forward and aft of the ends of the hatchways so as to provide in combination with the hatchways a maximum fore and aft feeding distance of 8 feet. Such openings shall be located approximately on the diagonal line between the hatch corners and the corners of the tween deck spaces.

144.20–28 (a) (4) The metacentric height maintained throughout the voyage (after correction for the free surface effects of liquids in tanks) shall not be less than 1¾ percent of the vessel's beam but not less than 12 inches in the case of one or two deck vessels and not less than 2 percent of the vessel's beam but not less than 14 inches in the case of other vessels.

144.20–28(a)(1)(2)(3)(4)

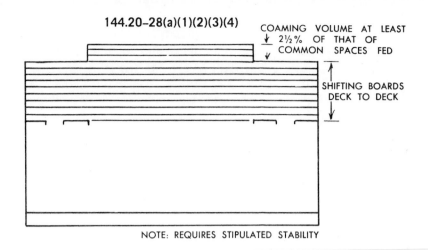

COAMING VOLUME AT LEAST
2½% OF THAT OF
COMMON SPACES FED

SHIFTING BOARDS
DECK TO DECK

NOTE: REQUIRES STIPULATED STABILITY

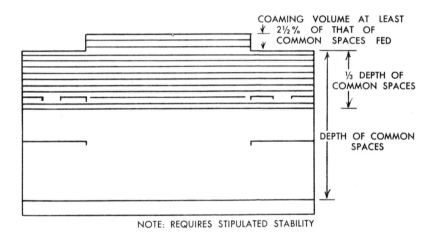

COAMING VOLUME AT LEAST
2½% OF THAT OF
COMMON SPACES FED

⅓ DEPTH OF
COMMON SPACES

DEPTH OF COMMON
SPACES

NOTE: REQUIRES STIPULATED STABILITY

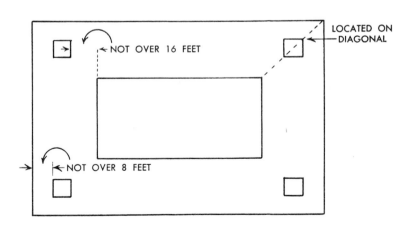

LOCATED ON
DIAGONAL

NOT OVER 16 FEET

NOT OVER 8 FEET

31

144.20–30 Bulk grain in tween decks and superstructures

144.20–30 (a) Bulk grain shall not be carried above deck, in the tween deck of a two deck vessel, or in the upper tween deck of a vessel having more than two decks except under the following conditions:

144.20–30 (a) (1) The bulk grain or other cargo shall be stowed so as to ensure maximum stability. The metacentric height maintained throughout the voyage (after correction for the free surface effects of liquids in tanks) shall not be less than 1¾ percent of the vessel's beam but not less than 12 inches in the case of one or two deck vessels, and not less than 2 percent of the vessel's beam but not less than 14 inches in the case of other vessels. Where specific data on metacentric height is not available, grain loaded above deck, in the tween deck of a two deck vessel, or in the uppermost tween deck of a vessel having more than two decks, shall not exceed 28 percent by weight of the total cargo below the space concerned; except that this limitation shall not apply when the grain carried above deck or in the uppermost tween deck is oats, barley, or cottonseed. The conditions in this subparagraph are in all cases subject to the additional condition that the master is satisfied that the ship will have adequate stability throughout the voyage.

144.20–30 (a) (2) The deck area of any portion of the spaces referred to in this section which contains bulk grain and which is only partly filled shall not exceed 1,000 square feet.

144.20–30 (a) (3) All spaces referred to in this section in which bulk grain is stowed shall be subdivided by transverse bulkheads at intervals of not more than 100 feet. When this distance is exceeded the excess space shall be entirely filled with bagged grain or other suitable cargo.

144.20–30(a)(2)

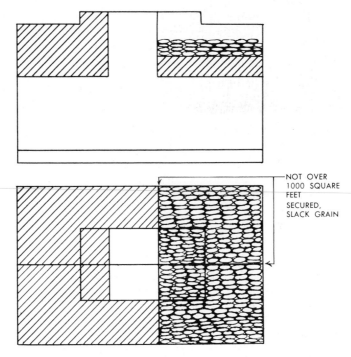

NOT OVER 1000 SQUARE FEET SECURED, SLACK GRAIN

144.20–30(a)(3)

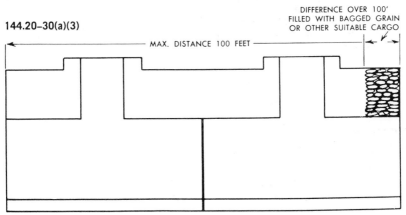

MAX. DISTANCE 100 FEET

DIFFERENCE OVER 100'
FILLED WITH BAGGED GRAIN
OR OTHER SUITABLE CARGO

144.20–32   Stowage of specially suitable ships

144.20–32(a) Ships which are generally of self-trimming type, specially designed and constructed for the carriage of bulk cargoes and having two or more vertical or sloping grain tight longitudinal divisions suitably disposed to limit the effect of any transverse shift of grain, may carry bulk grain without regard to the requirements of Sections 144.20–10 through 144.20–30 subject however to compliance with the following requirements:

144.20–32(a)(1) As many holds and compartments as possible shall be full and trimmed full.

144.20–32(a)(2) For any specified arrangement of stowage the metacentric height at any stage of the voyage (after correction for the free surface effects of liquids in tanks) shall be sufficient so that the list resulting from the heeling moment due to the following assumed shift of grain shall not exceed 5 degrees or the angle at which one-half the freeboard is immersed, if less.

144.20–32(a)(3) In all holds and compartments, grain surfaces are assumed to settle 2 percent by volume and at a slope of 30 degrees under all surfaces which have an inclination of less than 30 degrees to the horizontal. All resulting grain free surfaces except those sloping opposite to the direction of list (i.e., sloping towards the high side after list) are assumed to shift to an angle of 12 degrees with the original horizontal.

144.20–32(a)(4) However, any grain surfaces which are overstowed in accordance with section 144.20–22 shall be assumed to shift after settling, to an angle of 8 degrees with the original horizontal.

144.20–32(a)(5) Where the metacentric height necessary to compliance with the provisions of this section is considered to be excessive, the design of vessel will be required to be suitably modified or stowage in accordance with Sections 144.20–10 through 144.20–30 will be required.

144.20–32(a)(6) Where acceptance under the provisions of this section is desired, calculations relative to the anticipated loading and to the foregoing stability requirements shall be submitted to the Commandant, U.S. Coast Guard, for approval prior to commencement of construction. These will be subject to confirmation by a stability test as provided in Section 93.05–1 of Subchapter I (Cargo and Miscellaneous Vessels) of this chapter.

144.20–32(b) Where considered necessary, supplementary conditions shall be required either with respect to the vessel's design and construction, or with respect to particular loading precautions to prevent shifting of grain.

EXAMPLES OF TRANSVERSE SECTIONS OF
SPECIALLY SUITABLE SHIPS

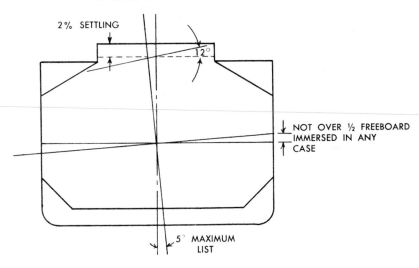

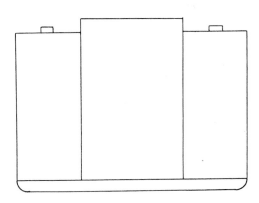

144.20-34   Stability conditions

144.20-34(a)   It is a condition of acceptance of loading based upon the stability limits specified in this subpart that the vessel shall be supplied with plans and stability data, approved by the Commandant, including the following information:

144.20-34(a)(1)   A capacity plan, including grain capacities and centers.

144.20-34(a)(2)   The minimum acceptable GM when carrying grain.

144.20-34(a)(3)   Stability data applicable to typical loading conditions for grain and other homogeneous cargoes when loaded at stowage factors of 45, 55, 65, 75 cubic feet per ton. Such data shall be given, in each case, both for typical departure and arrival conditions. Where an arrival condition includes salt water ballast, and an intermediate tankage condition results in a lesser GM, such intermediate condition shall also be given. In calculating the available GM, free surface allowance shall be made for all slack liquids, but in no case shall the free surface correction used be less than that corresponding to maximum free surface for the pair of tanks, port and starboard, of each type, having the largest free surface, plus the fuel oil settlers, plus the virtual free surface at 5 degrees heel for all nominally full fuel oil tanks (taken 98 percent full).

144.20-34(a)(4)   To provide for conditions wherein shifting boards may be omitted, as provided by Subparagraph 144.20-10 (b)(2), grain free surface applicable to feeders not fitted with shifting boards shall be given. In order to provide flexibility in the subsequent selection of feeder arrangements, this free surface shall be presented as a function of the aggregate length of feeders, grain density, and vessel displacement rather than as just applying to any specific grain stowage arrangement.

144.20-34(b)   The stability information supplied specially suitable ships shall, in general, comply with this section subject to such modification as is necessary, having regard for their special arrangements.

144.20-34(c)   Double bottom tanks having a width measured at half length in excess of 60 percent of the vessel's molded breadth shall in no case be permitted. Such tanks shall therefore be divided by a watertight longitudinal division.

144.20-36   Grain loading plans

144.20-36(a)   Vessels carrying grain shall be loaded in accordance with grain loading plans bearing the approval of the National Cargo Bureau, Inc., or of another agency otherwise officially designated. A grain loading plan shall take into account the applicable requirements of this subchapter and shall indicate the main characteristics of the fittings used to prevent the shifting of cargo. It shall indicate the distribution and the circumstances of loading. Additionally, in all cases where approval is dependent upon the stability limits specified in this subpart, it shall, in conjunction with the information called for by Section 144.20–34, indicate the applicable minimum GM and associated tankage conditions.

144.20–36 (b) A grain loading plan, in addition to the language in which it is given, shall be annotated in at least one other of the following languages: English, French, Spanish, or Russian.

144.20–36 (c) A copy of the grain loading plan shall be maintained at all times on the vessel. The master, if so required, shall produce it for the inspection of the appropriate authority of the port in which loading takes place.

144.20–36 (d) A grain loading plan and associated stability information approved for a vessel belonging to a country which is a party to the effective International Safety of Life at Sea Convention, issued either under the authority of the government of that country or under the authority of another government which is a party to that Convention upon the request of the first government, will be accepted by the United States. Other contracting governments have agreed to accept such information as evidence that the vessel, when loaded in accordance with this grain loading plan, meets the applicable grain loading requirements of the effective Convention.

144.20–36 (e) Vessels not having a grain loading plan approved in accordance with the paragraph (d) of this section may expect to be required to comply in detail with the rules of the country in which the loading port is situated.

144.30 VESSELS SHIFTING PORTS

144.30–1 Shifting vessels with part cargoes of loose grain in bulk

144.30–1 (a) The regulations in this subpart shall apply to vessels loaded with part cargoes of loose grain in bulk shifting between ports for the purpose of loading additional cargo and modify certain requirements under Subpart 144.20. Masters of all vessels shifting ports under these modified requirements shall check with the Weather Bureau to ascertain the forecast of the weather to be encountered on the voyage and shall not proceed under these conditions when unusually adverse weather conditions are indicated.

144.30–1 (b) Vessels subject to the regulations in this part, moving between ports totally within the inland waters of the United States, may load any amount of loose grain in bulk without securing the grain provided shifting boards extend above the grain in each hold at least 2 feet. Vessels that have no longitudinal bulkheads or shifting boards in the lower holds shall comply with Subparagraph 144.20–24 (a) (1).

144.30–1 (c) Vessels shifting between United States ports along the east coast as far south as Cape Henry, between Gulf ports, between Puget Sound ports and West Coast Canadian ports, between Puget Sound ports and Columbia River ports or between San Francisco, Los Angeles Harbor, and San Diego may load the following amounts without securing the grain provided the grain is covered with dunnage boards placed fore and aft and athwartship:

144.30–1 (c) (1) Any hold with less than 50 percent of its bulk grain capacity provided shifting boards extend above the grain in each hold at least 2 feet.

144.30–1 (c) (2) One hold with more than 50 percent of its bulk grain capacity and one other hold with less than 50 percent of its bulk grain capacity provided shifting boards extend above the grain in each hold at least 2 feet.

144.30–1 (c) (3) Where no longitudinal bulkheads or shifting boards are required to be erected, only two slack holds not exceeding the capacities specified in Subparagraph 144.20–24 (a) (1).

INDEX

NATIONAL CARGO BUREAU
NOTES ON BULK GRAIN REGULATIONS

Method of measuring depth of hatch coaming [paragraph 144.10–70(d)].

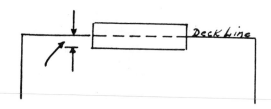

Method of measuring height of hatch coaming for computing bin feeder capacity or feeder capacity in single deck vessels.

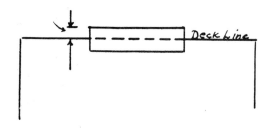

TWO DECKED SHIP WITH BRIDGE DECK
144.20–30

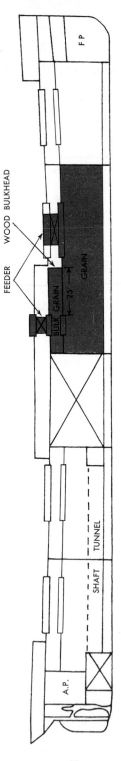

ILLUSTRATION OF HOW HEAVY GRAIN IN BULK MAY BE CARRIED IN THE 'TWEEN DECK OTHER THAN IN BINS AND FEEDERS.

FITTING OF WIRE STAYS
IN THE
ERECTION OF GRAIN SHIFTING BOARDS

The two diagrams which follow indicate the correct methods of applying wire stays in lieu of wood shores in erecting grain shifting boards. The first method provides for the use of an eye splice when erecting permanent or semi-permanent fittings. The second method provides for the use of not less than three wire clamps in lieu of the eye splice.

When using clamps, the nuts should be re-tightened after the stay has been put under tension in order to compensate for any decrease in the diameter of the wire caused by tension.

There are also two diagrams which show the *incorrect* methods of using wire stays. These methods are *not* approved and should never be used.

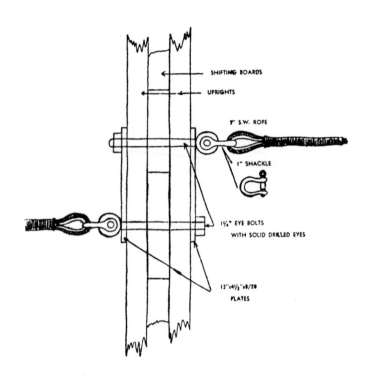

SHIFTING BOARDS

UPRIGHTS

3" S.W. ROPE

1" SHACKLE

1¼" EYE BOLTS
WITH SOLID DRILLED EYES

12"x4½"x8/20
PLATES

APPROVED METHOD OF FITTING WIRE STAYS FOR PERMANENT
OR SEMI-PERMANENT FITTINGS.

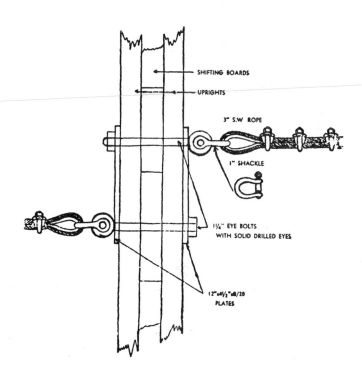

SHIFTING BOARDS

UPRIGHTS

3" S.W ROPE

1" SHACKLE

1¼" EYE BOLTS
WITH SOLID DRILLED EYES

12"x4½"x8/20
PLATES

APPROVED METHOD FOR USING CLAMPS IN THE ERECTION OF
GRAIN FITTINGS TO BE USED ONLY IN LIEU OF A WOOD SHORE.

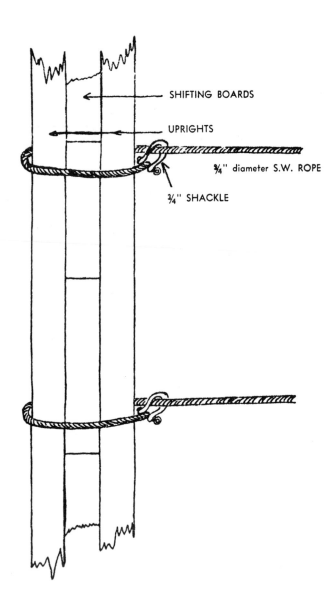

SHIFTING BOARDS

UPRIGHTS

¾" diameter S.W. ROPE

¾" SHACKLE

THIS METHOD OF SECURING SHIFTING BOARDS IS <u>NOT</u> APPROVED.

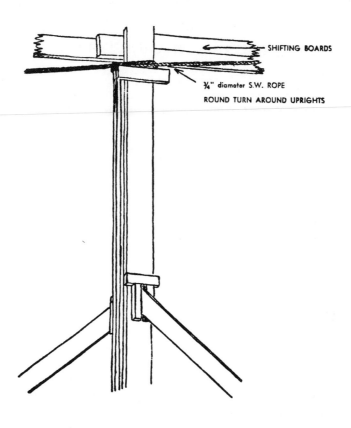

SHIFTING BOARDS

¾" diameter S.W. ROPE

ROUND TURN AROUND UPRIGHTS

THIS METHOD WITH ¾" WIRE AND ROUND TURN
AROUND UPRIGHTS NOT APPROVED.

USE OF STEEL STRAPPING
IN THE
INSTALLATION OF GRAIN FITTINGS

On April 5, 1956, the Operations Committee of National Cargo Bureau, Inc., recommended that the use of steel strapping be discontinued pending further study and analysis. This action was taken after reports from several vessels indicated that slackness had developed in the strapping, and it was the opinion of the Bureau that this defect was caused by the metal strapping biting into the wood uprights and by the lack of efficient setting up devices.

After a careful study of this defect, the Bureau concluded that it could be overcome by the adoption of certain improved methods of installation. Accordingly, on February 4, 1957 all National Cargo Bureau Surveyors were instructed to advise steamship owners and agents that steel strapping could be used in lieu of wood shores in the installation of grain fittings provided the installation, fittings and material were in accordance with the sketches which follow.

The steel strapping shall be of heavy duty commercial grade, 2" x .050" with minimum tensile strength of 11,000 pounds. The minimum tensile strength of the double strapping when used in the manner indicated herein would then be 22,000 pounds.

This equivalent arrangement is authorized under Section 144.10–90 of the Rules and Regulations for Bulk Grain Cargoes and applies only to vessels loading in U.S. Ports.

SUGGESTED METHODS OF USING STEEL STRAPPING AND FITTINGS IN THE INSTALLATION OF GRAIN FITTINGS

Figure I

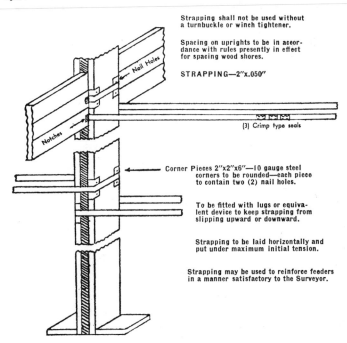

Strapping shall not be used without a turnbuckle or winch tightener.

Spacing on uprights to be in accordance with rules presently in effect for spacing wood shores.

STRAPPING—2"x.050"

(3) Crimp type seals

Corner Pieces 2"x2"x6"—10 gauge steel corners to be rounded—each piece to contain two (2) nail holes.

To be fitted with lugs or equivalent device to keep strapping from slipping upward or downward.

Strapping to be laid horizontally and put under maximum initial tension.

Strapping may be used to reinforce feeders in a manner satisfactory to the Surveyor.

Nail Holes

Notches

49

FITTINGS

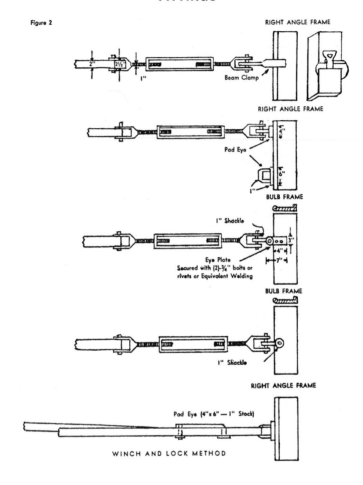

Figure 2

RIGHT ANGLE FRAME

2" 2½" 1" Beam Clamp

RIGHT ANGLE FRAME

Pad Eye

4" 6" 1"

BULB FRAME

1" Shackle

Eye Plate
Secured with (2)-¾" bolts or
rivets or Equivalent Welding

3" 4" 7"

BULB FRAME

1" Shackle

RIGHT ANGLE FRAME

Pad Eye (4"x 6" — 1" Stock)

WINCH AND LOCK METHOD

CARRIAGE OF BULK GRAIN IN TANK VESSELS

During World War II, tank vessels were used quite successfully for the carriage of grain in bulk without the use of shifting boards.

After the termination of the war, the matter did not again come under consideration until 1954 at which time trade conditions were such that operators approached National Cargo Bureau, Inc. with the request that they be permitted to reactivate the practice of carrying bulk grain in tank vessels. National Cargo Bureau, after careful study and discussions with various Classification Societies and the Department of Agriculture formulated certain requirements which were submitted to the U. S. Coast Guard.

A sample of the current Certificate of Readiness is shown below for information. Detailed instructions may be obtained from any office of National Cargo Bureau, Inc.

NATIONAL CARGO BUREAU, INC.

This is to Certify, that the_____of_____tons register, built

at_____whereof_____is Master and

now lying at_____is passed to load as follows:

BULK GRAIN (Tanks) Nos._____

_____

_____

said tanks having been prepared in accordance with the regulations of the Commandant of the United States Coast Guard so far as applicable, and in accordance with the recommendations of National Cargo Bureau, Inc.

The following items were noted at the time the vessel was passed to load:

Olfactory senses did not detect any traces of oil taint or of previous cargoes or other odors in all cargo tanks to be used for bulk grain cargo;

All cargo tanks to be used for bulk grain cargo appeared tight and showed no sign of leakage by visual inspection; stripping line suctions in the bottom of all cargo tanks, to be used for bulk grain cargo, were enclosed with a suitable box arrangement to allow water, in the event of leakage, to drain into these spaces; cargo tanks to be used for bulk grain cargo were also fitted with sounding pipes;

The main cargo suction lines to all cargo tanks which are to be used for bulk grain cargo were blanked off.

The vessel's hull in way of all cargo tanks to be used for bulk grain cargo had no cement boxes.

DATED at_____19____   Time passed_____

THIS IS NOT A CERTIFICATE OF SEAWORTHINESS

THE FOREGOING INSPECTION WAS UNDERTAKEN AND THIS CERTIFICATE OF READINESS IS ISSUED ON THE FOLLOW-ING TERMS AND CONDITIONS: While the Officers and Committees of National Cargo Bureau, Inc. use their best endeavors to insure that the functions of the Bureau are properly executed, neither such Officers nor such Committees, nor the Bureau nor its surveyors, employees, representatives or agents, are under any circumstances whatever to be held responsible for any inaccuracy in any report or certificate issued by the Bureau or its surveyors, or for any error of judgment, default, or negligence of the surveyors or other employees, representatives or agents of the Bureau.

No._____   _____Surveyor

PREPARING A SHIP BEFORE AND AFTER
CARRYING A GRAIN CARGO

The following suggestions are offered for officers of ships carrying grain cargoes.

It is essential that all spaces intended for grain be thoroughly clean, free of odor, and in every respect fit to receive the cargo. This means that the holds must be swept, washed, if necessary, and dried; bilges and wells cleaned; limber boards sealed with burlap or other approved material and properly secured.

Furthermore, vessels engaged in the grain trade will, no doubt, have a certain amount of infestation after carrying a grain cargo. It is claimed by some that it is difficult to find grain that is entirely free from insects. Therefore after the vessel has discharged her cargo, insects may be found in the compartments even in winter time when insect life is supposed to be dormant. A thorough cleaning in advance will go far to satisfy official requirements inasmuch as an inspection is made by the appropriate Government department for insect infestation in all compartments, and if they are found to be infested, the compartments will have to be fumigated before loading.

It is suggested that before tendering for a grain charter or going on berth for other delicate cargoes, vessels that have been engaged in the grain trade should be prepared as follows:

A thorough search should be made under ceiling boards, and in all crevices, cracks, beams, etc. taking a sample of the dust and debris accumulations and examining everything with flashlight and magnifying glass. Exposure to sufficient heat of an incandescent bulb will activate any dormant insect life present in the sample. This should be done before the hold is swept or cleaned. If insects are found, it is suggested that a steam hose under high pressure be used on all bulkheads and beams of the compartments or in any place where vermin can live. The compartment should then be allowed to dry and a further inspection made. If, after steaming the compartment, no insect life is found, it is reasonable to assume that the vessel would meet the requirements of the Department of Agriculture.

EXAMPLES OF STOWAGE ARRANGEMENTS FOR VARIOUS
STANDARD TYPE VESSELS

The arrangements which follow are intended as a guide in dealing with standard type vessels and represent a few of the many combinations made possible by the introduction of stability limits into the grain rules.

There are many variations of each of the types, and therefore operators should arrange their ships on an individual basis, taking into full consideration any characteristics not shown here.

It will be noted that there are many intermediate arrangements due to stowage factor, available deadweight and stability, making it impossible to illustrate all of them. Other arrangements will have to be dealt with individually.

The stability figures shown which include free surface corrections both for liquids and for grain free surface in feeders, are approximate and are not to be accepted for any one ship as such figures must be derived from data adjusted for particular vessels.

Form Rev. 7-62 (see Pages 105 to 107) may be employed, as applicable, to compute each vessel's stability where vessel is subject to stability limits. In making these calculations the light ship data and other related information should be that obtained from the vessel's approved stability information as required by 144.20-34 of CG-266.

DRAFTS AND FREEBOARDS OF
VARIOUS STANDARD TYPE VESSELS

Type	Summer Freeboard	Corresponding Draft
EC2-S-C1 (Liberty)	9' 08¾"	27' 08⅞"
VC2-S-AP2 (Victory)	9' 07"	28' 06¾"
C1-M-AV1	5' 08¼"	23' 05"
C2-S-B1	12' 05⅞"	27' 07⅞"
C-3	4' 07¾"	29' 05"
C4-S-A4	10' 10"	32' 09⅞"
C4-S-1d (Mariner)	5' 09½"	29' 10"

LIBERTY (EC2-S-C1) TYPE
Capacity and Tonnage

STOWAGE FACTORS

Compartment	Capacity	45 Tons	46 Tons	47 Tons	50 Tons	55 Tons	65 Tons	75 Tons
No. 1 Lower Hold	41257	917	897	878	825	750	635	550
No. 2 Lower Hold	98860	2197	2149	2103	1977	1797	1521	1318
No. 3 Lower Hold	68459	1521	1488	1457	1369	1245	1053	913
No. 4 Lower Hold	58841	1308	1279	1252	1177	1070	905	785
No. 5 Lower Hold	58620	1303	1275	1247	1172	1066	902	781
No. 1 & 2 Deep Tanks	22224	494	483	473	445	404	342	296
No. 3 Deep Tanks	26862	597	584	572	537	488	413	358
Total Holds	375123	8337	8155	7981	7502	6820	5771	5001
No. 1 Tweendeck	42924	954	933	913	858	780	660	572
No. 2 Tweendeck	46744	1039	1016	995	935	850	719	623
No. 3 Tweendeck	27970	622	608	595	559	509	430	373
No. 4 Tweendeck	35277	784	767	751	706	641	543	470
No. 5 Tweendeck	34570	768	752	736	691	629	532	461
Total Tweendecks	187485	4167	4076	3989	3749	3409	2884	2499
TOTALS	562608	12504	12231	11970	11251	10229	8655	7500

TANK CAPACITIES 100%

TANK	CAP. CU. FT.	BBLS. FUEL	TONS FUEL	TONS S.W.	TONS F.W.
Fore Peak	4845			138	
No. 1 D.B.	5045	896	133	144	
No. 2 D.B. Port	6041	1063	159	173	
No. 2 D.B. Stdb.	6041	1063	159	173	
No. 3 D.B. Port	4453	783	117	127	
No. 3 D.B. Stdb.	4453	783	117	127	
No. 4 D.B. Port	2412			69	67.2
No. 4 D.B. Stdb.	2412			69	67.2
No. 5 D.B. Port	4485	782	118	128	
No. 5 D.B. Stdb.	4485	782	118	128	
No. 6 D.B.	4191	733	110	120	
After Peak	5318			152	
No. 1 Deep Port	3983			114	
No. 1 Deep Stdb.	3983			114	
No. 2 Deep Port	7427			212	
No. 2 Deep Stdb.	7427			212	
No. 3 Deep Port	13583	2420	358	388	
No. 3 Deep Stdb.	13101	2320	345	374	
Fresh Water Port	987			28	27.0
Fresh Water Stdb.	987			28	27.0
Settling Port	1861	335	50		
Settling Stdb.	1861	335	50		
TOTALS		12295	1834	3018	188.4
Total Less Deeps		7755			

FUEL CONSUMPTION @ LOADED DRAFT

SPEED	BBLS/ 24 HR.	RANGE DAYS	
11	170	72	Max. Speed
10	150	81	Cruising Speed
9	130	94	
8	110	111	
6.5	80	153	

PORT CONSUMPTION IDLE 20 BBLS/DAY
PORT CONSUMPTION CARGO 35 BBLS/DAY

LIBERTY COAMINGS

	LENGTH	WIDTH	HEIGHT	CAPACITY
No. 1	33'-09"	20'	3'-00"	2025 cu. ft.
No. 2	35'-00"	20'	3'-00"	2100 cu. ft.
No. 3	20'-00"	20'	3'-00"	1200 cu. ft.
No. 4	33'-00"	20'	3'-00"	1980 cu. ft.
No. 5	35'-00"	20'	3'-00"	2100 cu. ft.

LIBERTY (EC2-S-C1) TYPE

9995 TONS (378851 BUSHELS) OF HEAVY GRAIN AT 47 CUBIC FEET PER TON. VOYAGE OF APPROXIMATELY 4000 MILES AT 10.5 KTS. VESSEL REQUIRED TO MAINTAIN 1.75% OF BEAM (57') OR 1.0 FT. GM THROUGHOUT VOYAGE (AFTER ALL CORRECTIONS).

LOAD DISPLACEMENT	14245T.
LIGHT SHIP	3400T.
SUMMER DEADWEIGHT	10845T.
CONSUMABLES	850T.
CARGO DEADWEIGHT	9995T.

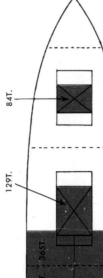
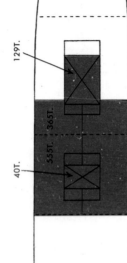
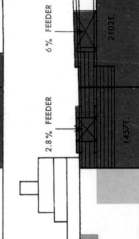

STABILITY:
DEPARTURE (APPROX.) 3.0 FT. GM
ARRIVAL (APPROX.) 2.4 FT. GM

DEPARTURE DATA

CONSUMABLES:
CREW, STORES AND FITTINGS 150T.
FRESH WATER (BLUE) 200T.
FUEL OIL (GREEN) 500T.
TOTAL 850T.

EST. MEAN SAILING DRAFT: 27'-08⅞"

LIBERTY (EC2-S-C1) TYPE

9995 TONS (378851 bu.) WHEAT CARGO AT 47 cu. ft./ton
REQUIRES 469765 cu. ft.

SPACE USED AS FOLLOWS:

LOWER HOLDS AND DEEP TANKS:		375123 cu. ft.	
FEEDERS:	No. 1 (3 Sect.)	3961	6.3%
	No. 2 (5 Sect.)	6048	6.1%
	No. 3 (2 Sect.)	1894	2.8%
	No. 4 (4 Sect.)	4231	7.2%
	No. 5 (4 Sect.)	4231	7.2%
TWEEN DECKS:	No. 3	26076	
	No. 4	31046	
	No. 2 (Aft)	17155	
	Total	469765 cu. ft.	

LIBERTY (EC2-S-C1) TYPE LOADED WITH LINSEED (FLAXSEED)

9800 TONS (434,677 bu.) LINSEED STOWING AT 55 CU. FT. PER TON.
VOYAGE OF APPROXIMATELY 5400 MILES AT 10.5 KTS.
VESSEL MUST MAINTAIN 1.0 FT. GM THROUGHOUT VOYAGE
(AFTER ALL CORRECTIONS).

DISPLACEMENT	14250T.
LIGHT SHIP	3400T.
DEADWEIGHT	10850T.
CONSUMABLES	1050T.
CARGO	9800T.

STABILITY:

DEPARTURE (APPROX.)	1.9 FT. GM
ARRIVAL (APPROX.)	1.1 FT. GM

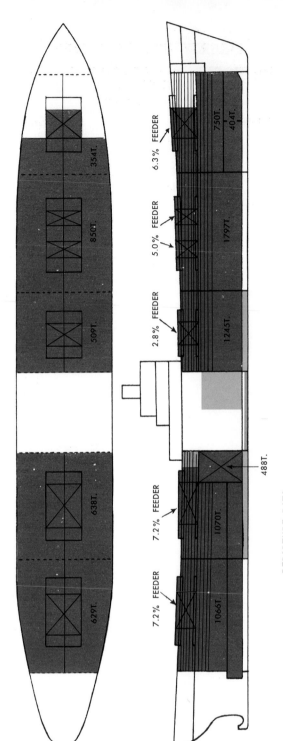

DEPARTURE DATA

CONSUMABLES:

CREW, STORES, FITTINGS	200T.
FRESH WATER (BLUE)	200T.
FUEL OIL (GREEN)	650T.
TOTAL	1050T.

EST. MEAN SAILING DRAFT: 27'-08⅞"

LIBERTY (EC2-S-C1) TYPE

9800 TONS (434677 bu.) LINSEED STOWING AT 55 cu. ft./ton
REQUIRES 539000 cu. ft.

SPACE USED AS FOLLOWS:

LOWER HOLDS AND DEEP TANKS		375123 cu. ft.	
FEEDERS:	No. 1 (3 Sec.)	3961	6.3%
	No. 2 (2 Sec.)	4836	5.0%
	No. 3 (2 Sec.)	1894	2.8%
	No. 4 (4 Sec.)	4231	7.2%
	No. 5 (4 Sec.)	4231	7.2%
COAMINGS:	No. 1	643	
	No. 2	1215	3.0%
	No. 3	744	2.9%
	No. 4	1086	3.5%
	No. 5	1086	3.5%
TWEENDECKS:	No. 1	14712	
	No. 2	40693	
	No. 3	25332	
	No. 4	29960	
	No. 5	29253	
TOTAL:		539000 cu. ft.	

LIBERTY (EC2-S-C1) TYPE

9995 TONS (453716 BUSHELS) HEAVY GRADE TWO ROWED BARLEY AT 49.5 LBS. PER BUSHEL STOWING AT 56.3 CUBIC FEET PER TON. VOYAGE OF APPROXIMATELY 4000 MILES AT 10.5 KTS. VESSEL REQUIRED TO MAINTAIN 1.75% OF BEAM (57') OR 1.0 FT. GM THROUGHOUT VOYAGE (AFTER ALL CORRECTIONS).

LOAD DISPLACEMENT	14245T.
LIGHT SHIP	3400T.
SUMMER DEADWEIGHT	10845T.
CONSUMABLES	850T.
CARGO DEADWEIGHT	9995T.

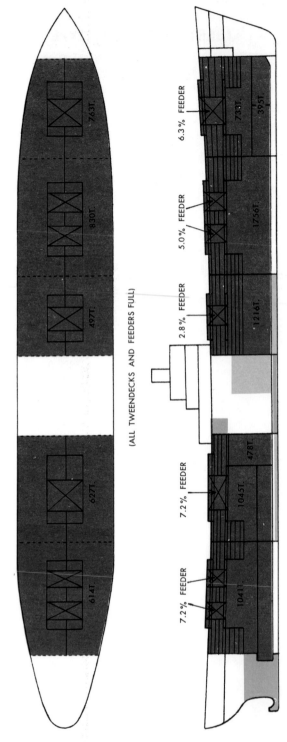

(ALL TWEENDECKS AND FEEDERS FULL)

DEPARTURE DATA

CONSUMABLES:

CREW, STORES AND FITTINGS	150T.
FRESH WATER (BLUE)	200T.
FUEL OIL (GREEN)	500T.
TOTAL	850T.

EST. MEAN SAILING DRAFT: 27'-0⅞"

STABILITY:

DEPARTURE (APPROX.) 1.3 FT. GM
ARRIVAL (APPROX.) 1.0 FT. GM (MAINTAINED BY BALLASTING AS FUEL IS BURNED).

LIBERTY (EC2-S-C1) TYPE

9995 TONS (453716 bu.) BARLEY AT 56.3 cu. ft./ton
VESSEL FULL CAPACITY 562608 cu. ft.

LOWER HOLDS AND DEEP TANKS:		375123 cu. ft.	
FEEDERS:	No. 1 (3 Sect.)	3961	6.3%
	No. 2 (2-2 Sect.)	4836	5.0%
	No. 3 (2 Sect.)	1894	2.8%
	No. 4 (4 Sect.)	4231	7.2%
	No. 5 (4 Sect.)	4231	7.2%
COAMINGS:	No. 1	1287	3.3%
	No. 2	1215	3.0%
	No. 3	744	2.9%
	No. 4	1086	3.5%
	No. 5	1086	3.5%
TWEEN DECKS:	No. 1	37676	
	No. 2	40693	
	No. 3	25332	
	No. 4	29960	
	No. 5	29253	
TOTAL:		562608 cu. ft.	

LIBERTY (EC2-S-C1) TYPE

LIGHT GRAIN

Space Available for **Light Grain** in Bulk:

Total Grain Capacity — 562608 cu. ft.

Total **Bulk Tonnages** Based on Total Bulk Capacity:

Barley	60 cu. ft./ton — 9377 tons
Oats	70 cu. ft./ton — 8037 tons
Cottonseed	75 cu. ft./ton — 7500 tons
Oats	87 cu. ft./ton — 6467 tons

VICTORY (VC2-S-AP2) TYPE
Capacity and Tonnage

		STOWAGE FACTOR							
Compartment	Capacity	45 Tons	46 Tons	47 Tons	50 Tons	55 Tons	56.3 Tons	65 Tons	75 Tons
No. 1 Lower Hold	32690	726	711	696	654	594	581	503	436
No. 2 Lower Hold	33095	735	719	704	662	602	588	509	441
No. 3 Lower Hold	62340	1385	1355	1326	1247	1133	1107	959	831
4 DT'S	42714	949	929	909	854	777	759	657	570
No. 4 Lower Hold	58675	1304	1276	1248	1174	1067	1042	903	782
No. 5 Lower Hold	32385	720	704	689	648	589	575	498	432
TOTAL HOLDS	261899	5819	5694	5572	5239	4762	4652	4029	3492
No. 2 Lower Tweendeck	25965	577	564	552	519	472	461	399	346
No. 3 Lower Tweendeck	44755	995	973	952	895	814	795	689	597
TOTAL TWEENDECKS	70720	1572	1537	1504	1414	1286	1256	1088	943
No. 1 Upper Tweendeck	28100	624	611	598	562	511	499	432	375
No. 2 Upper Tweendeck	30310	673	659	645	606	551	538	466	404
No. 3 Upper Tweendeck	50905	1131	1107	1083	1018	926	904	783	679
No. 4 Upper Tweendeck	54405	1209	1183	1158	1088	989	966	837	725
No. 5 Upper Tweendeck	49140	1092	1068	1046	983	893	873	756	655
TOTAL UPPER TWEENDECKS	212860	4731	4628	4530	4258	3871	3780	3275	2839
Foc'sle Deck	20925	465	455	445	419	380	372	322	279
TOTALS	566454	12587	12314	12056	11330	10299	10060	8714	7553

TANK CAPACITIES

FRAME	TANK	98% BBLS. FUEL	98% TONS FUEL	100% TONS S.W.	100% TONS F.W.
14- 37	No. 1 D.B. Port	862.0	130.0	141.1	
14- 37	No. 1 D.B. Stbd.	862.0	130.0	141.1	
37- 52	No. 2 D.B. Port	246.5	37.2	40.4	
37- 52	No. 2 D.B. Cntr.	600.5	90.5	98.3	
37- 52	No. 2 D.B. Stbd.	246.5	37.2	40.4	
52- 78	No. 3 D.B. Port	893.5	134.7	146.2	
52- 78	No. 3 D.B. Cntr.	1066.0	160.8	174.5	
52- 78	No. 3 D.B. Stbd.	893.5	134.7	146.2	
90- 95	No. 4 D.B. Port	173.5	26.2	28.4	
90- 95	No. 4 D.B. Stbd.	173.5	26.2	28.4	
95-122	No. 5 D.B. Port	538.5	81.2	88.1	
95-122	No. 5 D.B. Cntr.	1100.0	165.9	180.1	
95-122	No. 5 D.B. Stbd.	538.5	81.2	88.1	
95-110	No. 4A Deep Prt.	2350.5	354.5	384.8	
95-110	No. 4A Dp. Stbd.	2121.0	319.9	347.2	
110-122	No. 4B Deep Prt.	1577.0	237.8	258.1	
110-122	No. 4B Dp. Stbd.	1407.0	212.2	230.3	
122-139	No. 5 Deep Port	1427.5	215.3	233.7	
122-139	No. 5 Deep Stbd.	1186.0	178.9	194.1	
14-Fwd.	Fore Peak				106.0
147-Aft	After Peak				34.0
74- 78	F.O. Stng. Prt.	423.5	63.9	69.3	
74- 78	F.O. Stng. Stbd.	426.5	64.3	69.8	
74- 78	Distilled Water				21.2
79- 89	No. 4A D.B. Port-Res. Feed				55.1
79- 89	No. 4A D.B. Center-Res. Feed				65.7
79- 89	No. 4A D.B. Stbd.-Res. Feed				57.2
95- 99	Potable Water Center				95.7
	TOTALS	19113.5	2882.6	3268.6	294.9
	TOTALS LESS DEEPS	9044.5	1364.0	1620.4	

VICTORY COAMINGS

	LENGTH	WIDTH	HEIGHT	CAPACITY
No. 1	25'-00"	22'-04"	3'-00"	1674.75 cu. ft.
No. 2	24'-00"	22'-04"	3'-00"	1607.76 cu. ft.
No. 3	36'-00"	22'-04"	3'-00"	2411.64 cu. ft.
No. 4	36'-00"	22'-04"	3'-00"	2411.64 cu. ft.
No. 5	33'-00"	22'-04"	3'-00"	2210.67 cu. ft.

VICTORY (VC2-S-AP2) TYPE

9886 TONS (374711 BUSHELS) WHEAT STOWING AT 47 CU. FT. PER TON.
VOYAGE OF APPROXIMATELY 4000 MILES AT 15.5 KTS.
VESSEL MUST MAINTAIN 2% OF 62 FT. BEAM OR 1.2 FT. GM
THROUGHOUT VOYAGE.

LOAD DISPLACEMENT	15200T.
LIGHT SHIP	4464T.
DEADWEIGHT	10736T.
CONSUMABLES	850T.
CARGO	9886T.

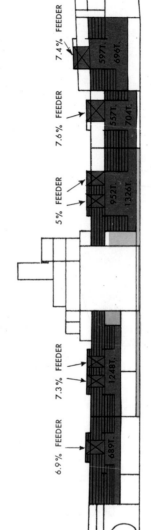

95T.

95T.

109T.

92T.

47T.

61.5T.

106T.

99T.

7.4% FEEDER

597T.

696T.

7.6% FEEDER

557T.

704T.

5% FEEDER

952T.

1326T.

7.3% FEEDER

1248T.

6.9% FEEDER

689T.

STABILITY:
DEPARTURE (APPROX.) 1.8 FT. GM
ARRIVAL (APPROX.) 1.6 FT. GM WITH 250T.
BALLAST.

DEPARTURE DATA

CONSUMABLES:

CREW, STORES, FITTINGS	150T.
FRESH WATER (BLUE)	200T.
FUEL OIL (GREEN)	500T.
TOTAL	850T.

EST. MEAN SAILING DRAFT: 28'-06¾"

VICTORY (VC2-S-AP2) TYPE

9886 TONS (374711 bu.) WHEAT AT 47 cu. ft./ton
REQUIRES 464642 cu. ft.

SPACE USED AS FOLLOWS:

(NO. 5 TWEEN DECK OPENED UP)

LOWER HOLDS		219185 cu. ft.	
NOS. 2 AND 3 LOWER TWEEN DECKS		70720	
NO. 1 TWEEN DECK		28100	
FEEDERS:	No. 1 (4 Sect.)	4470	7.4%
	No. 2 (4 Sect.)	4485	7.6%
	No. 3 (5 Sect.)	5116	5.0%
	No. 4 (4 Sect.)	4280	7.3%
	No. 5 (2 Sect.)	2244	6.9%
TWEEN DECKS:	No. 3 (Aft)	27801	
	No. 4	48585	
	No. 5	45785	
TWEEN DECK FEEDERS:	No. 3	780 } 390	4.2%
	No. 4	390 } 760 } 390	3.2%
	No. 5	1161	2.5%
TOTAL:		464642 cu. ft.	

VICTORY (VC2-S-AP2) TYPE (MODIFIED)

9886 TONS (374711 BUSHELS) WHEAT STOWING AT 47 CU. FT. PER TON.
VOYAGE OF APPROXIMATELY 4000 MILES AT 15.5 KTS.
VESSEL MUST MAINTAIN 2% OF 62 FT. BEAM OR 1.2 FT. GM THROUGHOUT THE
VOYAGE (AFTER ALL CORRECTIONS).

LOAD DISPLACEMENT	15200T.
LIGHT SHIP	4464T.
DEADWEIGHT	10736T.
CONSUMABLES	850T.
CARGO	9886T.

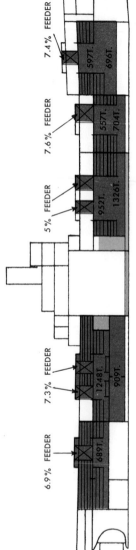

STABILITY:
DEPARTURE (APPROX.) 3.1 FT. GM
ARRIVAL (APPROX.) 2.7 FT. GM

DEPARTURE DATA

CONSUMABLES:
CREW, STORES, FITTINGS	150T.
FRESH WATER (BLUE)	200T.
FUEL OIL (GREEN)	500T.
TOTAL	850T.

EST. MEAN SAILING DRAFT: 28'-06¾"

VICTORY (VC2-S-AP2) TYPE (MODIFIED)

9886 TONS (374711 bu.) WHEAT AT 47 CU. FT. PER TON. REQUIRES 464642 CU. FT.

SPACE USED AS FOLLOWS:

LOWER HOLDS AND NO. 4 DEEP TANKS		261899 cu. ft.	
NOS. 2 AND 3 LOWER TWEEN DECKS		70720	
NO. 1 TWEEN DECK		28100	
FEEDERS:	No. 1 (4 Sect.)	4470	7.4%
	No. 2 (4 Sect.)	4485	7.6%
	No. 3 (5 Sect.)	5116	5.0%
	No. 4 (4 Sect.)	4280	7.3%
	No. 5 (2 Sect.)	2244	6.9%
TWEEN DECKS:	No. 4	35212	
	No. 5	45785	
TWEEN DECK FEEDERS:	No. 4	390 ⎫ 390 ⎬ 390 ⎭	3.3%
	No. 5	1161	2.5%
TOTAL:		464642 cu. ft.	

VICTORY (VC2-S-AP2) TYPE (MODIFIED)

9886 TONS (447053 BUSHELS) BARLEY STOWING AT 56.3 CU. FT. PER TON.
VOYAGE OF APPROXIMATELY 4000 MILES AT 15.5 KTS.
VESSEL MUST MAINTAIN 2% OF 62 FT. BEAM OR 1.2 FT. GM THROUGHOUT
VOYAGE (AFTER ALL CORRECTIONS).

LOAD DISPLACEMENT	15200T.
LIGHT SHIP	4464T.
DEADWEIGHT	10736T.
CONSUMABLES	850T.
CARGO	9886T.

198T.

53 8T.

904T.

966T.

873T.

5% FEEDER

499T.
581T.

5% FEEDER

461T.
588T.

5% FEEDER

5% FEEDER

795T.
1107T.

7.3% FEEDER

1042T.
759T.

6.9% FEEDER

575T.

STABILITY:
DEPARTURE (APPROX.) 2.5 FT. GM
ARRIVAL (APPROX.) 1.9 FT. GM

DEPARTURE DATA

CONSUMABLES:

CREW, STORES, FITTINGS	150T.
FRESH WATER (BLUE)	200T.
FUEL OIL (GREEN)	500T.
TOTAL	850T.

EST. MEAN SAILING DRAFT: 28'-06¾"

VICTORY (VC2-S-AP2) TYPE (MODIFIED)

9886 TONS (447053 bu.) BARLEY AT 56.3 cu. ft./ton
REQUIRES 556582 cu. ft.

SPACE USED AS FOLLOWS:

LOWER HOLDS AND NO. 4 DEEP TANKS		261899 cu. ft.	
NOS. 2 AND 3 LOWER TWEEN DECKS		70720	
NO. 1 TWEEN DECK		28100	
FEEDERS:	No. 1 (3 Sect.)	2856	5%
	No. 2 (3 Sect.)	2931	5%
	No. 3 (5 Sect.)	5116	5%
	No. 4 (4 Sect.)	4280	7.3%
	No. 5 (2 Sect.)	2244	6.9%
TWEEN DECKS:	No. 1	7258	
	No. 2	26597	
	No. 3	44239	
	No. 4	48585	
	No. 5	45785	
TWEEN DECK FEEDERS:	No. 1	939	
	No. 2	772	
	No. 3	1560	
	No. 4	1540	
	No. 5	1161	
TOTAL:		556582 cu. ft.	

VICTORY (VC2-S-AP2) TYPE

7478 TONS (422371 BUSHELS) OATS AT 70 CU. FT. PER TON.
VESSEL MUST MAINTAIN 2% OF 62 FT. BEAM OR 1.2 FT. GM THROUGHOUT
VOYAGE (AFTER ALL CORRECTIONS).

LOAD DISPLACEMENT	15200T.
LIGHT SHIP	4464T.
DEADWEIGHT	10736T.
CONSUMABLES	1050T.
BALLAST	1000T.
AVAILABLE	8686T.
USED	7478T.

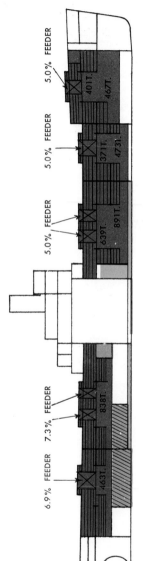

296T. 433T. 727T. 777T. 702T.

5.0% FEEDER
5.0% FEEDER
5.0% FEEDER
7.3% FEEDER
6.9% FEEDER

401T. 467T. 371T. 473T. 639T. 891T. 838T. 463T.

STABILITY:
DEPARTURE (APPROX.) 1.5 FT. GM WITH 1000Ts BALLAST.
ARRIVAL (APPROX.) 1.3 FT. GM WITH 1000Ts BALLAST.

DEPARTURE DATA

CONSUMABLES:

CREW, STORES, FITTINGS	150T.
FRESH WATER (BLUE)	200T.
FUEL OIL (GREEN)	700T.
TOTAL	1050T.

EST. MEAN SAILING DRAFT: 24'-11"

VICTORY (VC2-S-AP2) TYPE

7478 TONS (422371 bu.) FULL CARGO OATS AT 70 cu. ft./ton
TOTAL GRAIN CAPACITY — 523740 cu. ft.

LOWER HOLDS		219185 cu. ft.	
NO. 2 & 3 LOWER TWEEN DECKS		70720	
NO. 1 TWEEN DECK		28100	
TOTAL		318005	
FEEDERS:	No. 1 (3 Sect.)	2856	5.0%
	No. 2 (3 Sect.)	2931	5.0%
	No. 3 (5 Sect.)	5116	5.0%
	No. 4 (4 Sect.)	4280	7.3%
	No. 5 (2 Sect.)	2244	6.9%
TWEEN DECKS:	No. 1	17130	
	No. 2	26597	
	No. 3	44239	
	No. 4	48585	
	No. 5	45785	
TWEEN DECK FEEDERS:	No. 1	939	5.2%
	No. 2	772	2.9%
	No. 3	1560	3.5%
	No. 4	1540	3.2%
	No. 5	1161	2.5%
TOTAL:		523740 cu. ft.	

VICTORY (VC2-S-AP2) TYPE

LIGHT GRAIN

Space Available for **Light Grain** in Bulk:
Total **Bulk Tonnages** Based on Total Bulk Capacity: Total Grain Capacity—523740 cu. ft.

Barley	60 cu. ft./ton — 8729 tons
Oats	70 cu. ft./ton — 7482 tons
Cottonseed	75 cu. ft./ton — 6983 tons
Oats	87 cu. ft./ton — 6020 tons

C1-M-AV1 TYPE
Capacity and Tonnage

Compartment	Capacity	STOWAGE FACTOR						
		45 Tons	46 Tons	47 Tons	50 Tons	55 Tons	65 Tons	75 Tons
No. 1 Lower Hold	28025	623	609	596	561	510	431	374
No. 1 Tweendeck	26740	594	581	569	535	486	411	357
Total	54765	1217	1191	1165	1095	996	843	730
No. 2 Lower Hold	60545	1345	1316	1288	1211	1101	931	807
No. 2 Tweendeck	42290	940	919	900	846	769	651	564
Total	102835	2285	2236	2188	2057	1870	1582	1371
No. 3 Lower Hold	52095	1158	1133	1108	1042	947	801	695
No. 3 Tweendeck	38680	860	841	823	774	703	595	516
Total	90775	2017	1973	1931	1816	1650	1397	1210
No. 4 Lower Hold	7354	163	160	156	147	134	113	98
No. 4 Lower Tweendeck	11927	265	259	254	239	217	183	159
No. 4 Trunk	921	20	20	20	18	17	14	12
Total	20202	449	439	430	404	367	311	269
Grand Total	268577	5968	5838	5714	5373	4884	4130	3582

FUEL OIL & WATER BALLAST

Tank	Frames	Center of Gravity From C.L.	Abv. B.L.	Diesel Oil 98% Full Gallons	Barrels	Tons	S.W. Ballast 100% Full Tons
Fuel Oil							
Double Bottom No. 3P	72-102	− 31.48	1.61	20765	494.5	65.4	80.9
Double Bottom No. 3S	72-102	− 31.48	1.61	20765	494.5	65.4	80.9
Double Bottom No. 3C	72-102	− 32.00	1.56	30215	719.5	95.2	117.8
Double Bottom No. 4P	102-124	− 85.42	1.70	10110	240.5	31.8	39.4
Double Bottom No. 4S	102-124	− 85.42	1.69	9990	238.0	31.5	38.9
Double Bottom No. 4C	102-124	− 92.89	1.54	14530	346.0	45.8	56.6
Daily Service Tank P	121-124	−111.86	25.21	2300	55.0	7.2	—
Daily Service Tank S	121-124	−111.86	25.21	2300	55.0	7.2	—
Settling Tank P	121-124	−111.86	25.28	2340	55.5	7.4	—
Settling Tank S	121-124	−111.86	25.28	2340	55.5	7.4	—
Total Fuel Oil				115655	2754.0	364.3	—
Reserve Fuel Oil or Cargo Oil							
Double Bottom No. 1P	18- 37	+ 98.59	1.70	12265	292.0	38.6	47.8
Double Bottom No. 1S	18- 37	+ 98.12	1.69	12660	301.5	39.9	49.3
Double Bottom No. 2P	37- 72	+ 40.24	1.62	23415	557.5	73.8	91.3
Double Bottom No. 2S	37- 72	+ 40.24	1.62	23415	557.5	73.8	91.3
Double Bottom No. 2C	37- 72	+ 41.13	1.56	33400	843.0	111.5	138.0
Deep Tank	9- 18	+131.02	12.42	50845	1210.5	160.2	198.2
Total Reserve Fuel Oil or Cargo Oil				158000	3762.0	497.8	—
Grand Total — Diesel Oil and Water Ballast				273655	6516.0	862.1	1030.4

FRESH WATER

Tank	Frames	Center of Gravity From C.L.	Abv. B.L.	100% Full Gallons	Tons
Washing and Potable Water — Port	124-134	−124.18	7.60	6870	25.5
Washing and Potable Water — Stbd.	124-132	−122.89	7.65	4515	16.8
Total Washing and Potable Water				11385	42.3
Engine Circulating Water — D.B. No. 5	125-134	−126.11	1.71	7560	28.1
Forepeak	Stem-9	+148.00	14.31	15540	57.7
Afterpeak	138-Stern	−151.07	18.64	12160	45.1
Grand Total — Fresh Water				46645	173.2

C1-M-AV1 TYPE

5494 TONS (203806 bu.) WHEAT STOWING AT 46 CU. FT. PER TON.
VOYAGE APPROXIMATELY 1300 MILES AT 11 KTS.
VESSEL MUST MAINTAIN 1.0 FT. GM THROUGHOUT VOYAGE
(AFTER ALL CORRECTIONS).

DISPLACEMENT	8370T.
LIGHT SHIP	2342T.
DEADWEIGHT	6028T.
CONSUMABLES	420T.
CARGO	5608T.
USED	5494T.

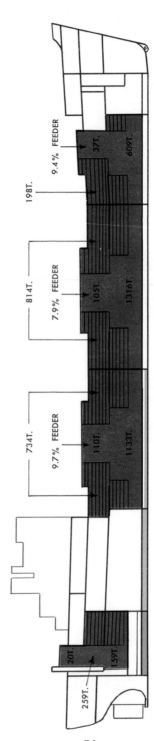

198T.

9.4% FEEDER
37T.
609T.

814T.

7.9% FEEDER
105T.
1316T.

734T.

9.7% FEEDER
110T.
1133T.

259T.
20T.
159T.

DEPARTURE DATA

CONSUMABLES:
CREW, STORES & FITTINGS	113T.
FRESH WATER (BLUE)	116T.
FUEL OIL (GREEN)	180T.
LUBE OIL	11T.
TOTAL	420T.

EST. MEAN SAILING DRAFT: 23'-01½"

STABILITY:
DEPARTURE (APPROX.) 2.48 FT. GM
ARRIVAL   (APPROX.) 2.48 FT. GM

C1-M-AV1 TYPE

5494 TONS (203806 bu.) WHEAT STOWING AT 46 cu. ft./ton
REQUIRES 252724 cu. ft.

SPACE USED AS FOLLOWS:

LOWER HOLDS:	No. 1	28025 cu. ft.	
	No. 2	60545	
	No. 3	52095	
	No. 4	7354	
FEEDERS:	No. 1	2640	9.4%
	No. 2	4811	7.9%
	No. 3	5059	9.7%
TWEENDECKS:	No. 1*	8715	
	No. 2	36534	
	No. 3	32871	
	No. 4	11927	
TWEENDECK FEEDERS:	No. 1	385	4.4%
	No. 2	945	2.6%
	No. 3	895	2.7%
TRUNK:	No. 4	921	4.8%
TOTAL:		253722 cu. ft.	

*Two Bins Aft

C2-S-B1 TYPE
Capacity and Tonnage

Compartment	Capacity	STOWAGE FACTORS						
		45 Tons	46 Tons	47 Tons	50 Tons	55 Tons	65 Tons	75 Tons
No. 1 Lower Hold	43762	972	951	931	875	796	673	583
No. 2 Deep Tanks	69211	1538	1505	1473	1384	1258	1065	923
No. 3 Lower Hold	68034	1512	1479	1448	1361	1237	1047	907
No. 4 Deep Tanks	64406	1431	1400	1370	1288	1171	991	859
No. 5 Lower Hold	48080	1068	1045	1023	962	874	740	641
TOTAL HOLDS	293493	6522	6380	6245	5870	5336	4515	3913
No. 1 Lower Tweendeck	22672	504	493	482	453	412	349	302
No. 2 Lower Tweendeck	37808	840	822	804	756	687	582	504
No. 3 Lower Tweendeck	43406	965	944	924	868	789	668	579
No. 4 Lower Tweendeck	42174	937	917	897	843	767	649	562
TOTAL LOWER TWEENDECKS	146060	3246	3175	3107	2921	2656	2247	1947
No. 1 Upper Tweendeck	25548	568	555	544	511	465	393	341
No. 2 Upper Tweendeck	37476	833	815	797	750	681	577	500
No. 3 Upper Tweendeck	42708	949	928	909	854	777	657	569
No. 4 Upper Tweendeck	42394	942	922	902	848	770	652	565
No. 5 Upper Tweendeck	31346	697	681	667	627	570	482	418
TOTAL UPPER TWEENDECKS	179472	3988	3902	3819	3589	3263	2761	2393
TOTAL	619025	13756	13457	13171	12380	11255	9523	8254

TANK CAPACITIES 100%

Tank	Cap. Cu. Ft.	Bbls. Fuel	Tons Fuel	Tons S.W.	Tons F.W.
Fore Peak	3156			90.1	
No. 1 D.B. Port	3333	593	90.0	95.2	
No. 1 D.B. Stbd.	3333	593	90.0	95.2	
No. 2 D.B. Port	5766	1027	155.7	164.7	
No. 2 D.B. Stbd.	5766	1027	155.7	164.7	
No. 3 D.B. Port	7506	1337	202.7	214.4	
No. 3 D.B. Stbd.	7456	1328	200.9	213.0	
No. 4 D.B. Port	3918			111.9	108.8
No. 4 D.B. Stbd.	3918			111.9	108.8
No. 5 D.B. Port	5420	965	146.3	154.8	
No. 5 D.B. Stbd.	5420	965	146.3	154.8	
No. 6 D.B. Port	1648	293	44.5	47.0	
No. 6 D.B. Stbd.	1648	293	44.5	47.0	
After Peak	2626			75.8	
No. 2 Deep Port	17815			509.0	
No. 2 Deep Stbd.	17312			494.6	
No. 2A Deep Port	17024			486.4	
No. 2A Deep Stbd.	16555			473.0	
No. 4 Deep Port	18613			531.8	
No. 4 Deep Stbd.	19013			543.2	
No. 4A Deep Port	13201			377.1	
No. 4A Deep Stbd.	13579			387.7	
No. 5 Deep Port	4171	743	112.6	119.2	
No. 5 Deep Stbd.	3829	682	103.4	109.4	
No. 5A Deep Port	2110	375	56.9	60.3	
No. 5A Deep Stbd.	1803	318	48.7	51.5	
Settling Port	2697	480	72.8		
Settling Stbd.	2697	480	72.8		
Distilled Water	976			27.8	27.1
Fresh Water	6185			176.1	171.8
TOTALS		11499	1743.8		416.5
Total Less Deeps		9381			

FUEL CONSUMPTION @ LOADED DRAFT

Speed	Bbls./ 24 Hrs.	Range Days	
17	280	41	Max. Speed
15.5	240	47	Cruising Speed
PORT CONSUMPTION IDLE		20 BBLS./DAY	
PORT CONSUMPTION CARGO		35 BBLS./DAY	

C2-S-B1 COAMINGS

	LENGTH	WIDTH	HEIGHT	CAPACITY
No. 1	27'-00"	20'-00"	3'-00"	1620 cu. ft.
No. 2	32'-06"	20'-00"	3'-00"	1950 cu. ft.
No. 3	35'-00"	20'-00"	3'-00"	2100 cu. ft.
No. 4	30'-00"	20'-00"	3'-00"	1800 cu. ft.
No. 5	30'-00"	20'-00"	3'-00"	1800 cu. ft.

C2-S-B1 TYPE

9641 TONS (357650 BUSHELS) WHEAT AT 46 CU. FT. PER TON.
VOYAGE OF APPROXIMATELY 3850 MILES AT 15.0 KTS.
MUST MAINTAIN 2% OF 63 FT. BEAM OR 1.3 FT. GM THROUGHOUT VOYAGE
(AFTER ALL CORRECTIONS).

LOAD DISPLACEMENT	14995T.
LIGHT SHIP	4493T.
SUMMER DEADWEIGHT	10502T.
CONSUMABLES	861T.
CARGO DEADWEIGHT	9641T.

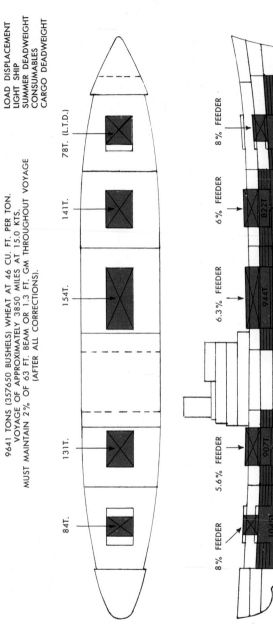

84T.   131T.   154T.   141T.   78T. (L.T.D.)

8% FEEDER   5.6% FEEDER   6.3% FEEDER   6% FEEDER   8% FEEDER

1045T.   907T.   944T.   822T.   951T.
1400T.   1479T.   1505T.

STABILITY:
DEPARTURE (APPROX.) 3.1 FT. GM
ARRIVAL (APPROX.) 2.7 FT. GM

DEPARTURE DATA

CONSUMABLES:
CREW, STORES, FITTINGS	161T.
FRESH WATER (BLUE)	200T.
FUEL OIL (GREEN)	500T.
TOTAL	861T.

EST. MEAN SAILING DRAFT: 27'-07⅞"

C2-S-B1 TYPE

9641 TONS (357650 bu.) WHEAT STOWING AT 46 cu. ft./ton
REQUIRES 443486 cu. ft.

SPACE USED AS FOLLOWS:

LOWER HOLDS & LOWER TWEEN DECKS	(EXCEPT NO. 1 LOWER TWEEN DECK)	416881 cu. ft.	
FEEDERS:			
	No. 1 L.T.D. (4 Sect.)	3610	8%
	No. 2 U.T.D. (6 Sect.)	6479	6%
	No. 3 U.T.D. (7 Sect.)	7106	6.3%
	No. 4 U.T.D. (6 Sect.)	6061	5.6%
	No. 5 U.T.D. (4 Sect.)	3971	8%
TOTAL:		444108 cu. ft.	

C2-S-B1 TYPE

9452 TONS (429151 BUSHELS) BARLEY AT 56.3 CU. FT. PER TON.
VOYAGE OF APPROXIMATELY 5800 MILES AT 15.0 KNOTS.
MUST MAINTAIN 2% OF 63 FT. BEAM OR 1.3 FT. GM THROUGHOUT
VOYAGE (AFTER ALL CORRECTIONS).

LOAD DISPLACEMENT   14995T.
LIGHT SHIP   4493T.
SUMMER DEADWEIGHT   10502T.
CONSUMABLES   1050T.
CARGO   9452T.

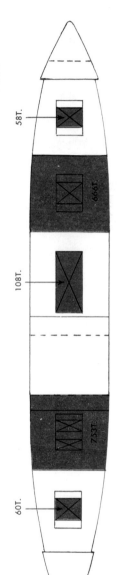

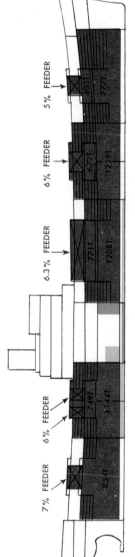

DEPARTURE DATA

CONSUMABLES:
CREW, STORES, FITTINGS   150T.
FRESH WATER (BLUE)   200T.
FUEL OIL (GREEN)   700T.
TOTAL   1050T.

EST. MEAN SAILING DRAFT: 27'-07⅞"

STABILITY:
DEPARTURE (APPROX.) 1.6 FT. GM
ARRIVAL (APPROX.) 1.3 FT. GM
(MAINTAINED BY BALLASTING AS FUEL IS BURNED OFF.)

C2-S-B1 TYPE

9452 TONS (429151 bu.) BARLEY STOWING AT 56.3 cu. ft./ton
REQUIRES 532147 cu. ft.

SPACE USED AS FOLLOWS:

LOWER HOLDS & LOWER TWEENDECKS:			
		439553 cu. ft.	
FEEDERS:	No. 1	3290	5%
	No. 2	2239	6%
	No. 3	7106	6.3%
	No. 4	2541	6.0%
	No. 5	3388	7.0%
TOTAL:		18564	
COAMINGS:	No. 2	1278	3.8%
	No. 4	1019	2.6%
TOTAL:		2297	
TWEEN DECKS:	No. 2	33959	
	No. 4	38834	
TOTAL:		72793	
GRAND TOTAL:		533207 cu. ft.	

C-3 TYPE
Capacity and Tonnage
STOWAGE FACTORS

Compartment	Capacity	45 Tons	46 Tons	47 Tons	50 Tons	55 Tons	65 Tons	75 Tons
No. 1 Lower Hold	49600	1102.2	1078.2	1055	992.0	901.5	763.0	661.3
No. 2 Deep Tanks	65120	1447.0	1415.7	1386	1302.4	1184.0	1001.8	868.3
No. 3 Lower Hold	84770	1883.8	1842.8	1804	1695.4	1541.3	1304.1	1130.2
No. 4 Deep Tanks	62900	1397.8	1367.4	1338	1258.0	1143.7	967.7	838.6
Total Holds	**262390**	**5830.8**	**5704.1**	**5583**	**5247.8**	**4770.5**	**4036.6**	**3498.4**
No. 1 Lower Tween Deck	47270	1050.4	1027.6	1006	945.4	859.5	727.2	630.2
No. 2 Lower Tween Deck	59610	1324.8	1295.8	1268	1192.2	1083.8	917.0	794.8
No. 3 Lower Tween Deck	66160	1470.2	1438.2	1408	1323.2	1202.9	1017.8	882.1
No. 4 Lower Tween Deck	56340	1252.0	1224.8	1199	1126.8	1024.4	866.7	751.2
No. 5 Lower Tween Deck	72330	1607.3	1572.4	1539	1446.6	1315.0	1112.7	964.4
Total Lower Tween Decks	**301710**	**6704.7**	**6558.8**	**6420**	**6034.2**	**5485.6**	**4641.4**	**4022.7**
No. 1 Upper Tween Deck	34060	756.9	740.4	725	681.2	619.2	524.0	454.1
No. 2 Upper Tween Deck	39500	877.8	858.7	840	790.0	718.1	607.6	526.6
No. 3 Upper Tween Deck	34290	762.0	745.4	730	685.8	623.4	527.5	457.2
No. 4 Upper Tween Deck	45770	1017.0	995.0	974	915.4	832.2	704.1	610.2
No. 5 Upper Tween Deck	43750	972.2	951.0	931	875.0	799.4	673.0	583.3
Total Upper Tween Decks	**197370**	**4385.9**	**4290.5**	**4200**	**3947.4**	**3592.3**	**3036.2**	**2631.4**
GRAND TOTAL	**761470**	**16921.4**	**16553.4**	**16203**	**15229.4**	**13848.4**	**11714.2**	**10152.5**

TANK CAPACITIES

Tank	Cap. Cu. Ft.	Bbls. Fuel	Tons Fuel	100% Tons S.W.	Tons F.W.	98% Tons C.O.
Fore Peak	4252			121.5		
No. 1 D.B. Port	3034	540	81.4	86.7		
No. 1 D.B. Stbd.	3034	540	81.4	86.7		
No. 2 D.B. Port	4557	805	122.4	130.2		
No. 2 D.B. Stbd.	5789	1030	155.4	165.4		
No. 3 D.B. Port	8302	1478	222.8	237.2		
No. 3 D.B. Stbd.	9320	1765	266.9	283.4		
No. 4 D.B. Port	5280			151.0	146.7	
No. 4 D.B. Stbd.	5521			157.6	153.3	
No. 5 D.B. Port	5974	1063	160.4	170.7		
No. 5 D.B. Stbd.	5761	1026	154.7	164.6		
No. 6 D.B. Port	2058	366	55.2	58.8		
No. 6 D.B. Stbd.	2058	366	55.2	58.8		
After Peak	2807	500	75.2	80.2		80.2
Settling Port	2579	459	69.2			
Settling Stbd.	2579	459	69.2			
Fresh Water Port	1245				34.6	
Fresh Water Stbd.	1245				34.6	
Distilled Water	648				18.0	
No. 2 Deep Port	15490			442.5		380.0
No. 2 Deep Stbd.	15490			442.5		380.0
No. 2A Deep Port	17360			496.0		424.8
No. 2A Deep Stbd.	17360			496.0		424.8
No. 4 Deep Port	20090			574.0		495.6
No. 4 Deep Stbd.	20160			576.0		497.3
No. 4A Deep Port	12310			351.7		303.4
No. 4A Deep Stbd.	11750			335.7		289.4
No. 5 Deep Port	5460			156.0		134.3
No. 5 Deep Stbd.	4700			134.3		115.6
No. 5A Deep Port	2404	437	65.0	68.7		60.2
No. 5A Deep Stbd.	1809	342	48.8	51.7		47.2
TOTALS		**11176**	**1682.6**		**387.2**	**3632.8**

FUEL CONSUMPTION @ LOADED DRAFT

Speed	Bbls./24 Hrs.	Range Days	
18.0	428	44	Max. Speed
16.5	320	57	Cruising Speed
10.0	135	140	
9.0	120	157	
8.0	105	180	
6.5	95	210	

C-3 COAMINGS

	Length	Width	Height	Capacity
No. 1	36'-00"	20'-00"	3'-00"	2160 cu. ft.
No. 2	30'-00"	24'-00"	3'-00"	2160 cu. ft.
No. 3	37'-06"	24'-00"	3'-00"	2700 cu. ft.
No. 4	30'-00"	24'-00"	3'-00"	2160 cu. ft.
No. 5	40'-00"	20'-00"	3'-00"	2400 cu. ft.

C-3 TYPE

11546 TONS (672901 BUSHELS) WHEAT STOWING AT 47 CU. FT. PER TON.
VOYAGE OF APPROXIMATELY 3300 MILES AT 16 KTS.
VESSEL MUST MAINTAIN 2% OF 69.5 FT. BEAM OR 1.4 FT. GM THROUGHOUT
VOYAGE (AFTER ALL CORRECTIONS).

DISPLACEMENT 18216T.
LIGHT SHIP 5820T.
DEADWEIGHT 12396T.
CONSUMABLES 850T.
CARGO 11546T.

77T.   127T.   160T.   133T.   53T. (L.T.D.)

5% FEEDER

1538T.   1199T.   1338T.   1408T.   1804T.   1268T.   1386T.   1055T.

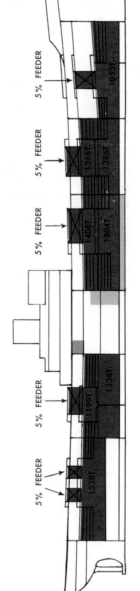

DEPARTURE DATA

CONSUMABLES:
CREW, STORES, FITTINGS 150T.
FRESH WATER (BLUE) 200T.
FUEL OIL (GREEN) 500T.
TOTAL 850T.

EST. MEAN SAILING DRAFT: 29'-05"

STABILITY:
DEPARTURE (APPROX.) 3.5 FT. GM
ARRIVAL (APPROX.) 3.1 FT. GM

C-3 TYPE

11546 TONS (672901 bu.) WHEAT AT 47 cu. ft./ton
REQUIRES 542662 cu. ft.

SPACE USED AS FOLLOWS:

LOWER HOLDS:	No. 1-4	262390 cu. ft.	
LOWER TWEEN DECKS:	No. 2-5	254440	
	Total	516830	
FEEDERS:	No. 1 L.T.D.	2492	5%
	No. 2 U.T.D.	6252	5%
	No. 3 U.T.D.	7520	5%
	No. 4 U.T.D.	5969	5%
	No. 5 U.T.D.	3599	5%
	Total:	25832	
	Grand Total:	542662 cu. ft.	

C-3 TYPE

9286 TONS (614089 BUSHELS) OATS AT 34 LBS. PER BU. STOWING AT 82 CU. FT.
PER TON. VOYAGE OF APPROXIMATELY 7100 MI. AT 16 KTS.
VESSELS MUST MAINTAIN 2% OF 69.5 FT. BEAM OR 1.4 FT. GM THROUGHOUT
VOYAGE (AFTER ALL CORRECTIONS).

DISPLACEMENT	18216T.
LIGHT SHIP	5820T.
DEADWEIGHT	12396T.
CONSUMABLES	1350T.
CARGO DEADWEIGHT	11046T.
USED	9286T.
LIGHT	1760T.

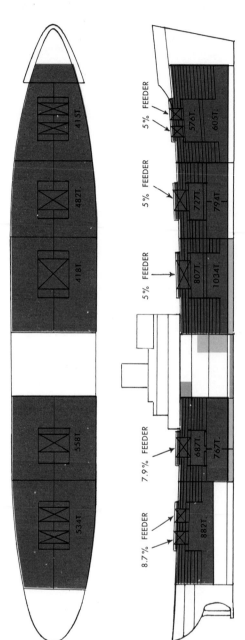

DEPARTURE DATA

CONSUMABLES:
CREW, STORES, FITTINGS	150T.
FRESH WATER (BLUE)	200T.
FUEL OIL (GREEN)	1000T.
TOTAL	1350T.

EST. MEAN SAILING DRAFT: 26'-11"

STABILITY:
DEPARTURE (APPROX.) 1.8 FT. GM
ARRIVAL (APPROX.) 1.4 FT. GM

86

C-3 TYPE

9286 TONS (614089 bu.) OATS 34 lbs./bu. STOWING AT 82 cu. ft./ton

SPACE USED AS FOLLOWS:

LOWER HOLDS:		262390 cu. ft.	
LOWER TWEEN DECKS:		301710	
	Total	564100	
FEEDERS:	No. 1	4680	5%
	No. 2	6252	5%
	No. 3	7520	5%
	No. 4	4431	7.9%
	No. 5	3872	8.7%
	Total	26755	
TWEEN DECKS:	No. 1	28503	
	No. 2	32466	
	No. 3	25988	
	No. 4	40415	
	No. 5	38090	
	Total	165462	
TWEEN DECK FEEDERS:	No. 1	877	3%
	No. 2	782	2.5%
	No. 3	782	3.0%
	No. 4	924	2.5%
	No. 5	1788	4.7%
	Total	5153	
TOTAL:		761470 cu. ft.	

C4-S-A4 TYPE
Capacity and Tonnage

Compartment	Capacity	45 Tons	46 Tons	47 Tons	50 Tons	55 Tons	65 Tons	75 Tons
No. 1 L. H.	7283	161.9	158.3	155	145.6	132.5	112.0	97.0
No. 2 L. H.	35163	781.4	764.4	748	703.2	639.3	540.9	468.8
No. 3 DTS.	43396	964.4	943.4	923	867.9	789.0	667.6	578.6
No. 4 L. H.	45780	1017.3	995.2	974	915.6	832.3	704.3	610.4
No. 5 L. H.	45741	1016.5	994.3	973	914.8	831.6	703.7	609.9
No. 6 L. H.	75863	1685.8	1649.0	1614	1517.3	1379.3	1167.0	1011.5
Total	253226	5627.3	5504.6	5387	5064.4	4604.0	3895.5	3376.2
1st Platform								
No. 1	6663	148.0	144.8	142	133.3	121.0	102.5	88.8
No. 2	28387	630.8	617.0	604	567.7	516.0	436.7	378.5
No. 4	34490	766.4	749.8	734	689.8	627.0	530.6	459.9
No. 5	34490	766.4	749.8	734	689.8	627.0	530.6	459.9
No. 7	7452	165.6	162.0	159	149.0	135.5	114.6	99.3
Total	111482	2477.2	2423.4	2373	2229.6	2026.5	1715.0	1486.4
3rd Deck								
No. 1	8035	178.6	174.7	171	160.7	146.0	123.6	107.1
No. 2	29125	647.2	633.0	620	582.5	529.5	448.0	388.3
No. 3	32497	722.0	706.4	692	649.9	590.9	499.9	433.3
No. 4	34490	766.4	749.8	734	689.8	627.0	530.6	459.9
No. 5	34490	766.4	749.8	734	689.8	627.0	530.6	459.9
No. 6	34220	760.4	743.9	728	684.4	622.1	526.4	456.2
No. 7	10793	239.8	234.6	230	215.8	196.2	166.0	143.9
Total	183650	4080.8	3992.2	3909	3672.9	3338.7	2825.1	2448.6
2nd Deck								
No. 1	11148	247.7	242.3	237	222.9	202.7	171.5	148.6
No. 2	30643	680.1	666.0	652	612.8	557.0	471.4	408.7
No. 3	34124	758.3	741.8	726	682.5	620.4	525.0	454.9
No. 4	36238	805.3	787.8	771	724.8	658.8	557.5	483.2
No. 5	34896	775.5	758.6	742	697.9	634.5	536.8	465.2
No. 6	35582	790.7	773.5	757	711.6	646.9	547.4	474.4
No. 7 Inc. Reefer	17799	395.5	386.9	379	356.0	323.6	273.8	237.3
Total	200430	4453.1	4356.9	4264	4008.5	3643.9	3083.4	2672.3
Upper Deck								
No. 1	12944	287.6	281.3	275	258.9	235.0	199.0	172.6
No. 2	21841	485.4	474.8	465	436.8	397.0	336.0	291.2
No. 7	15118	336.0	328.6	322	302.4	274.9	232.5	201.6
Total	49903	1109.0	1084.7	1062	998.1	906.9	767.5	665.4
Grand Total	798691	17747.4	17361.8	16995	15973.5	1452.0	12286.5	10648.9

FUEL OIL & SALT WATER BALLAST

No.	Tanks	Frames	C. of G. From C.L.	Abv. B.L.	Fuel Oil 98% Full Gal's.	Barrels	Tons	S.W. Ballast 100% Full
1-P	Double Bottom	13- 32	197.4F.	4.4	17820	424.0	64.0	69.5
1-S	Double Bottom	13- 32	197.4F.	4.4	17820	424.0	64.0	69.5
2-P	Double Bottom	37- 58	134.7F.	2.8	14410	343.0	51.6	56.2
2-C	Double Bottom	32- 57	148.6F.	2.5	52550	1251.5	188.7	204.8
2-S	Double Bottom	37- 58	134.7F.	2.8	14410	343.0	51.6	56.2
3-P	Double Bottom	58- 80	85.4F.	2.5	31230	743.5	112.1	121.7
3-C	Double Bottom	58- 79	88.3F.	2.5	44160	1051.5	158.6	172.1
3-S	Double Bottom	58- 80	85.4F.	2.5	31230	743.5	112.1	121.7
4-P	Double Bottom	80-102	31.8F.	2.5	38190	909.5	137.1	148.8
4-C	Double Bottom	80-101	33.3F.	2.5	44690	1064.0	160.5	174.2
4-S	Double Bottom	80-102	31.8F.	2.5	38190	909.5	137.1	148.8
5-P	Double Bottom	102-124	22.2A.	2.5	36780	876.0	132.1	143.4
5-C	Double Bottom	102-123	21.7A.	2.5	44600	1062.0	160.2	173.8
5-S	Double Bottom	102-124	22.2A.	2.5	36780	876.0	132.1	143.4
6-P	Double Bottom	124-146	74.6A.	2.6	23840	567.5	85.6	92.9
6-C	Double Bottom	124-145	76.7A.	2.5	44360	1056.0	159.3	172.9
6-S	Double Bottom	124-146	74.6A.	2.6	23840	567.5	85.6	92.9
	Totals				554900	13212.0	1992.3	2162.8
	Fore Peak	13 Fwd.	230.6F.	14.8	—	—	—	82.5
	After Peak	194 Aft.	230.8A.	28.2	—	—	—	167.0
	Total							249.5
	F.O. Settling P.	172-178	176.9A.	12.4	9990	238.0	35.9	—
	F.O. Settling S.	172-181	180.0A.	12.5	10360	246.5	37.2	—
	Totals				20350	484.5	73.1	—
	Grand Totals				575250	13696.5	2065.4	2412.3

FRESH WATER

No.	Tanks	Frames	C. of G. From C.L.	Abv. B.L.	Gallons	Tons
7-P	Feed Water Double Bottom	147-172	134.6A.	2.8	24090	89.5
7-S	Double Bottom	147-172	134.3A.	2.8	24560	91.2
8-P	Double Bottom	172-188	186.2A.	2.9	6990	25.9
8-S	Double Bottom	172-188	186.2A.	2.9	6990	25.9
	Distilled Water P.	168-171	164.4A.	11.5	1798	6.7
	Distilled Water S	168-171	164.4A.	11.5	1798	6.7
	Total Feed Water				66226	245.9
	Drinking Water 3rd Dk. Port	154-159	130.8A.	30.9	12430	46.43
	3rd Dk. Stdb.	155-159	133.0A.	30.9	8900	33.23
	Total Drinking Water				21330	79.86
	Total Fresh Water				87556	325.56

LUBRICATING & DIESEL OIL

Tanks	Frames	C. of G. From C.L.	Abv. B.L.	Gal.	Full To Overflow Barrels	Tons
L.O. Settling P.	159-164	144.4A.	30.5	1915	45.6	6.0
L.O. Storage P.	159-162	142.0A.	30.4	1920	45.7	6.0
Diesel Emergency Gen. CL	150-152	118.4A.	74.1	355	8.5	1.2
Diesel Galley & Cold Start CL	150-152	118.4A.	74.1	1610	38.3	5.4

GENERAL PARTICULARS
FUEL CONSUMPTION @ LOADED DRAFT

Speed	Bbls./24 Hrs.	Range Days	
18.5	480	29	Max. Speed
16.0	360	38	Cruising Speed
10.0	175	78	
9.0	160	86	
8.0	145	94	
6.5	130	103	

FUEL CAPACITY	13696.5 BBLS.
PORT CONSUMPTION IDLE	65 BBLS. PER 24 HRS.
PORT CONSUMPTION CARGO	75 BBLS. PER 24 HRS.

C4-S-A4 TYPE

13979 TONS (518576 bu.) WHEAT STOWING AT 46 CU. FT. PER TON.
VOYAGE OF APPROX. 3000 MILES AT 16.0 KTS.
VESSEL MUST MAINTAIN 2% OF 71.7 FT. BEAM OR 1.4 FT. GM
(AFTER ALL CORRECTIONS).

LOAD DISPLACEMENT	22000T.
LIGHT SHIP	7171T.
DEADWEIGHT	14829T.
CONSUMABLES	850T.
CARGO	13979T.

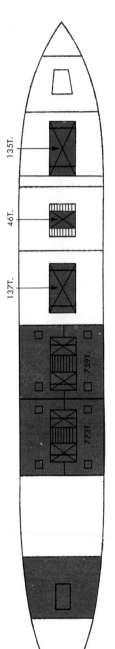

Note: Trimming Hatches cut in Third Deck (also see note below).

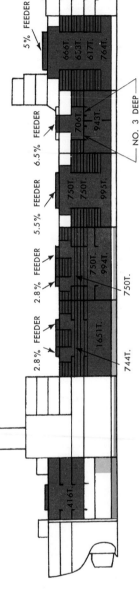

Note: This method of loading a multiple deck vessel, which is not specifically provided for in Chapter VI of the 1960 Safety of Life at Sea Convention, may be used as an equivalent if platform deck in Hold No. 5 is opened and the plans for same, together with arrangement plans for the carriage of grain, are approved by National Cargo Bureau, Inc.

STABILITY:
DEPARTURE (APPROX.) 3.9 FT. GM
ARRIVAL (APPROX.) 3.5 FT. GM

DEPARTURE DATA

CONSUMABLES:

CREW, FITTINGS, STORES	150T.
FRESH WATER (BLUE)	200T.
FUEL OIL (GREEN)	500T.
TOTAL	850T.

EST. MEAN SAILING DRAFT: 32'-09⅞"

C4-S-A4 TYPE

13979 TONS (518576 bu.) WHEAT STOWING AT 46 cu. ft./ton
REQUIRES 643034 cu. ft.

SPACE USED AS FOLLOWS:

NOS. 2, 3, 4, 5 & 6 LOWER HOLDS		245943 cu. ft.	
NOS. 2, 4 & 5 1ST PLATFORM		97367	
NOS. 2, 3, 4, 5 & 6 3RD DECK		164822	
NO. 2 2ND DECK		30643	
TOTAL		538775	
FEEDERS:	No. 2	6216	5.4%
	No. 3	2112	6.5%
	No. 4	6336	5.5%
	No. 5	3168	2.8%
	No. 6	3168	2.8%
NO. 5 2ND DECK		30756	
NO. 6 2ND DECK		31442	
TWEENDECK FEEDERS:	No. 5	972	3.6%
	No. 6	972	3.0%
NO. 7 UPPER TWEENDECK		6500	
2ND DECK		9000	
3RD DECK		3636	
GRAND TOTAL:		643153 cu. ft.	

C4-S-A4 TYPE

13977 TONS (634600 bu.) BARLEY STOWING AT 56.3 CU. FT. PER TON.
VOYAGE OF APPROXIMATELY 3000 MILES AT 16.0 KTS.
VESSEL MUST MAINTAIN 2% OF 71.7 FT. BEAM OR 1.4 FT. GM
(AFTER ALL CORRECTIONS).

LOAD DISPLACEMENT	22000T.
LIGHT SHIP	7171T.
DEADWEIGHT	14829T.
CONSUMABLES	852T.
CARGO USED	13977T.

29T.

Note: Trimming Hatches cut in Third Deck (also see note below)

638T.

606T.

644T.

620T.

632T.

→ FORECASTLE DECK
→ UPPER DECK
→ SECOND DECK
→ THIRD DECK
→ PLATFORM DECK

5.3% FEEDER

198T.
143T.
118T.
129T.

2.9% FEEDER

517T.
504T.
630T.

544T.

577T.
776T.

NO. 3 DEEP
TANK LIDS
IN PLACE

5.4% FEEDER

613T.
813T.

613T.

613T.

2.8% FEEDER

3% FEEDER

613T.
812T.

613T.

2.8% FEEDER

607T.

1353T.

2.8% FEEDER

885T.

Note: This method of loading a multiple deck vessel, which is not specifically provided
for in Chapter VI of the 1960 Safety of Life at Sea Convention, may be used as an
equivalent if platform decks in Holds Nos. 2, 4, and 5 are opened and the plans for
same, together with arrangement plans for the carriage of grain, are approved by
National Cargo Bureau, Inc.

STABILITY:
DEPARTURE (APPROX.) 2.0 FT. GM
ARRIVAL (APPROX.) 1.4 FT. GM

DEPARTURE DATA

CONSUMABLES:

CREW, FITTINGS, STORES	150T.
FRESH WATER (BLUE)	202T.
FUEL OIL (GREEN)	500T.
TOTAL	852T.

EST. MEAN SAILING DRAFT: 32'-09⅝"

92

C4-S-A4 TYPE

13977 TONS (634600 bu.) BARLEY STOWING AT 56.3 cu. ft./ton
REQUIRES 786905 cu. ft.

SPACE USED AS FOLLOWS:

ALL LOWER HOLDS:		253226 cu. ft.	
FIRST PLATFORM:		111482	
THIRD DECK:		183650	
SECOND DECK:	No. 1	11148	
	No. 2	30643	
	No. 7	17799	
FEEDERS:	No. 2	1760	5.3%
	No. 3	3168	2.5%
	No. 4	1760	5.4%
	No. 5	3168	2.8%
	No. 6	3168	2.8%
	No. 7	3168	2.8%
UPPER TWEENDECKS:	No. 2	18133	
	No. 3	31392	
	No. 4	32098	
	No. 5	30756	
	No. 6	31442	
	No. 7	15118	
TWEENDECK FEEDERS:	No. 2	540	2.9%
	No. 3	972	2.9%
	No. 4	972	3.0%
	No. 5	972	3.0%
	No. 6	972	3.0%
TOTAL:		987507 cu. ft.	

C4-S-A4 TYPE

10753 TONS (607030 bu.) OATS STOWING AT 70 CU. FT. PER TON.
VOYAGE OF APPROXIMATELY 5500 MI. AT 16.0 KTS.
VESSEL MUST MAINTAIN 2% OF 71.7 FT. BEAM OR 1.4 FT. GM
(AFTER ALL CORRECTIONS).

LOAD DISPLACEMENT	22000T.
LIGHT SHIP	7171T.
DEADWEIGHT	14829T.
CONSUMABLES	1350T.
CARGO	13479T.
USED	10753T.

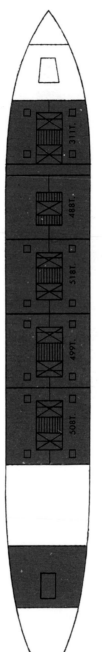

Note: Trimming Hatches cut in Third Deck (also see note below)

FORECASTLE DECK
UPPER DECK
SECOND DECK
THIRD DECK
PLATFORM DECK

2.5% FEEDER
5.4% FEEDER
2.8% FEEDER
2.8% FEEDER
2.8% FEEDER
2.8% FEEDER

311T.
488T.
518T.
499T.
508T.

438T.
416T.
406T.
502T.
464T.
620T.
493T.
654T.
493T.
653T.
493T.
1084T.
489T.

NO. 3 DEEP
TANK LIDS
IN PLACE

Note: This method of loading a multiple deck vessel, which is not specifically provided for in Chapter VI of the 1960 Safety of Life at Sea Convention, may be used
as an equivalent if platform decks in Holds Nos. 2, 4, and 5 are opened and the
plans for same, together with arrangement plans for the carriage of grain, are
approved by National Cargo Bureau, Inc.

DEPARTURE DATA

CONSUMABLES:

CREW, FITTINGS, STORES	150T.
FRESH WATER (BLUE)	200T.
FUEL OIL (GREEN)	1000T.
TOTAL	1350T.

STABILITY:
DEPARTURE (APPROX.) 1.7 FT. GM
ARRIVAL (APPROX.) 1.4 FT. GM
WITH BALLASTING AS FUEL IS USED.
(NO. 1 HOLD LEFT EMPTY FOR TRIM PURPOSES.)

216T.
254T.
154T.
107T.

EST. MEAN SAILING DRAFT: 29'-02¾"

C4-S-A4 TYPE

10753 TONS (607030 bu.) OATS STOWING AT 70 cu. ft./ton
REQUIRES 752718 cu. ft.

SPACE USED AS FOLLOWS:

NOS. 2, 3, 4, 5 AND 6 LOWER HOLDS:		245943 cu. ft.	
NOS. 2, 4, 5 AND 7-1ST PLATFORMS:		104819	
NOS. 2, 3, 4, 5, 6 AND 7 3RD DECKS:		175615	
NOS. 2 AND 7-2ND DECKS:		48442	
	No. 3-2nd Deck	31392	
	No. 4-2nd Deck	32098	
	No. 5-2nd Deck	30756	
	No. 6-2nd Deck	31442	
FEEDERS:			
	No. 2	3168	2.5%
	No. 3	1760	5.4%
	No. 4	3168	2.8%
	No. 5	3168	2.5%
	No. 6	3168	2.8%
	No. 7	3308	
UPPER DECKS:			
	No. 2	18133	
	No. 7	11618	
TWEENDECK FEEDERS:			
	No. 2	540	2.9%
	No. 3	972	3.0%
	No. 4	972	2.9%
	No. 5	972	3.6%
	No. 6	972	3.0%
	No. 7	292	2.5%
TOTAL:		752718 cu. ft.	

MARINER (C4-S-1d) TYPE

Capacity and Tonnage

Dry Cargo Compartments	Capacity	STOWAGE FACTORS							
		45	46	47	50	55	65	70	75
Hold No. 1 Maindeck	19485	433	424	415	390	354	300	278	260
2nd Deck	20750	461	451	442	415	377	319	296	277
3rd Deck	15175	337	330	323	304	276	233	217	202
Total No. 1 Hold	55410	1231	1205	1180	1108	1007	852	791	739
Hold No. 2 2nd Deck	34385	764	748	732	688	625	529	491	458
3rd Deck	39020	867	848	830	780	709	600	557	520
Hold	29135	647	633	620	583	530	448	416	388
Total No. 2 Hold	102540	2279	2229	2182	2051	1864	1578	1464	1367
Hold No. 3 2nd Deck	49155	1092	1069	1046	983	894	756	702	655
3rd Deck	63970	1422	1391	1361	1279	1163	984	914	853
Hold	57590	1280	1260	1225	1152	1047	886	823	768
Total No. 3 Hold	170715	3794	3711	3632	3414	3104	2626	2439	2276
Hold No. 4 2nd Deck	48050	1068	1045	1022	961	874	739	686	641
3rd Deck	65385	1453	1421	1391	1308	1189	1006	934	872
Hold	67945	1510	1477	1446	1359	1235	1045	971	906
Total No. 4 Hold	181380	4031	3943	3859	3628	3298	2790	2591	2418
Hold No. 5 2nd Deck	47680	1060	1037	1014	954	867	734	681	636
26'-6" Flat	17190	382	373	366	344	313	264	246	229
3rd Deck (CL)	17220	382	374	366	344	314	265	246	230
Hold (P)	22870	508	497	487	457	416	352	327	305
Hold (S)	21095	469	459	449	421	384	325	301	281
Total No. 5 Hold	126055	2801	2740	2682	2521	2292	1939	1801	1681
Hold No. 6 2nd Deck	46240	1028	1005	984	925	841	711	661	617
3rd Deck	72980	1622	1587	1553	1460	1327	1123	1043	973
Hold (P)	6695	149	146	142	134	122	103	96	89
Hold (S)	6695	149	146	142	134	122	103	96	89
Total No. 6 Hold	132610	2947	2883	2821	2652	2411	2040	1896	1768
Hold No. 7 2nd Deck	29135	647	633	620	583	530	448	416	388
3rd Deck	39460	877	858	840	789	717	607	564	526
Total No. 7 Hold	68595	1524	1491	1460	1372	1247	1055	980	915
Total Dry Cargo	837305	18606	18202	17816	16746	15224	12880	11962	11164

FUEL OIL AND BALLAST

Compartment		Tons F.O. 98%	Tons S.W. 100%	VCG	LCG F.P.
No. 1 D.B. Tank	Frs. 14- 24C	48.65	52.80	4.53	39.9
No. 1A D.B. Tank	Frs. 24- 36C	82.75	89.81	4.80	64.9
No. 2 D.B. Tank	Frs. 36- 57P	71.93	78.06	2.71	106.6
No. 2 D.B. Tank	Frs. 36- 57S	71.93	78.06	2.71	106.6
No. 3 D.B. Tank	Frs. 57- 82C	229.91	249.53	2.50	161.1
No. 3 D.B. Tank	Frs. 57- 82P	56.21	61.01	2.95	169.2
No. 3 D.B. Tank	Frs. 57- 82S	56.21	61.01	2.95	169.2
No. 4 D.B. Tank	Frs. 82-106C	226.41	245.73	2.47	222.0
No. 4 D.B. Tank	Frs. 82-106P	129.47	140.52	2.64	223.8
No. 4 D.B. Tank	Frs. 82-106S	129.47	140.52	2.64	223.8
No. 5 D.B. Tank	Frs. 106-127C	198.19	215.10	2.46	278.3
No. 5 D.B. Tank	Frs. 106-134P	179.86	195.21	2.62	288.3
No. 5 D.B. Tank	Frs. 106-134S	181.87	197.39	2.61	288.3
No. 6 D.B. Tank	Frs. 134-160C	244.84	265.73	2.46	354.4
No. 6 D.B. Tank	Frs. 134-160P	87.93	95.44	2.84	348.2
No. 6 D.B. Tank	Frs. 134-160S	87.93	95.44	2.84	348.2
No. 7 D.B. Tank	Frs. 160-184P	95.56	103.72	2.72	412.4
No. 7 D.B. Tank	Frs. 160-184S	95.56	103.72	2.72	412.4
*No. 1 Deep Tank	Frs. 14- 24C	126.63	137.44	16.49	40.3
*No. 1A Deep Tank	Frs. 24- 36C	260.28	282.50	16.79	65.1
No. 2 Deep Tank Sett.	Frs. 106-113P	101.75	————	19.05	260.8
No. 2 Deep Tank Sett.	Frs. 106-113S	101.75	————	19.05	260.8
No. 3 Deep Tank Sett.	Frs. 113-119P	86.96	————	19.11	277.0
No. 3 Deep Tank Sett.	Frs. 113-119S	86.96	————	19.11	277.0
*No. 6 Deep Tank	Frs. 160-172P	203.32	220.67	11.44	401.2
*No. 6 Deep Tank	Frs. 160-172S	203.32	220.67	11.44	401.2
*No. 7 Deep Tank	Frs. 172-184P	130.08	141.18	11.73	430.7
*No. 7 Deep Tank	Frs. 172-184S	130.08	141.18	11.73	430.7
*No. 8 Deep Tank	Frs. 184-190P	51.05	55.41	9.63	454.0
*No. 8 Deep Tank	Frs. 184-190S	51.05	55.41	9.63	454.0
Fore Peak	Stem.-Fr. 14C	————	110.84	11.65	17.1
Aft Peak	Frs. 204-218C	————	92.98	24.90	506.8
Total Fuel Oil & Ballast		3807.91	3927.08	†7.50	†267.3

*These Tanks Fitted For Cargo Fuel Oil
†Centers For Fuel Oil Only

FRESH WATER

Compartment		Tons F.W. 100%	VCG	LCG F.P.
No. 4 Deep Tank	Frs. 120-127P/S	123.68	21.32	296.0
No. 5 Deep Tank	Frs. 127-133P/S	108.41	20.90	312.0
Distilled Water	Frs. 106-109C	24.90	39.50	255.8
Total Fresh Water		256.99	22.90	298.8

MARINER COAMINGS

	Length	Width	Height	Capacity
No. 1	20'-03"	18'-06"	2'-07"	966.5 cu. ft.
No. 2	30'-00"	24'-00"	2'-08"	1915.2 cu. ft.
No. 3	40'-00"	30'-00"	2'-08"	3192.0 cu. ft.
No. 4	40'-00"	30'-00"	2'-08"	3192.0 cu. ft.
No. 5	40'-00"	30'-00"	2'-08"	3192.0 cu. ft.
No. 6	40'-00"	30'-00"	2'-08"	3192.0 cu. ft.
No. 7	25'-00"	30'-00"	2'-08"	1995.0 cu. ft.

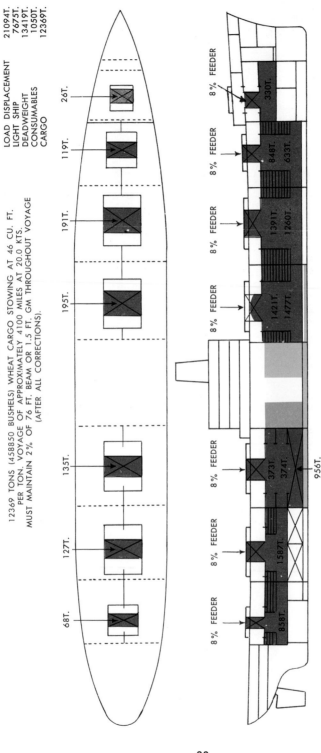

MARINER (C4-S-ld) TYPE

12369 TONS (458850 BUSHELS) WHEAT CARGO STOWING AT 46 CU. FT. PER TON. VOYAGE OF APPROXIMATELY 4100 MILES AT 20.0 KTS. MUST MAINTAIN 2% OF 76 FT. BEAM OR 1.5 FT. GM THROUGHOUT VOYAGE (AFTER ALL CORRECTIONS).

LOAD DISPLACEMENT	21094T.
LIGHT SHIP	7675T.
DEADWEIGHT	13419T.
CONSUMABLES	1050T.
CARGO	12369T.

26T.   119T.   191T.   195T.   135T.   127T.   68T.

8% FEEDER

330T.   848T.   633T.   1391T.   1260T.   1421T.   1477T.   373T.   374T.   956T.   1587T.   858T.

DEPARTURE DATA

CONSUMABLES:

CREW, STORES, FITTINGS	150T.
FRESH WATER (BLUE)	200T.
FUEL OIL (GREEN)	700T.
TOTAL	1050T.

EST. MEAN SAILING DRAFT: 29'-10"

STABILITY:
DEPARTURE (APPROX.) 5.6 FT. GM
ARRIVAL (APPROX.) 4.9 FT. GM

MARINER (C4-S-Id) TYPE

12369 TONS (458850 bu.) WHEAT STOWING AT 46 cu. ft./ton

SPACE USED AS FOLLOWS:

LOWER HOLDS:	No. 1	15175 cu. ft.	
	No. 2	29135	
	No. 3	57590	
	No. 4	67945	
	No. 5	43965	
	No. 6	72980	
	No. 7	39460	
TOTAL:		326250	
LOWER TWEEN DECKS:	No. 2	39020	
	No. 3	63970	
	No. 4	65385	
TRUNKWAY:	No. 5	34410	
TOTAL:		202785	
FEEDERS:	No. 1	1214	8%
	No. 2	5452	8%
	No. 3	9725	8%
	No. 4	10666	8%
	No. 5	6270	8%
	No. 6	5834	8%
	No. 7	3157	8%
TOTAL:		42318	
GRAND TOTAL:		571353 cu. ft.	

99

MARINER (C4-S-ld) TYPE

12369 TONS (561593 BUSHELS) BARLEY AT 56.3 CU. FT. PER TON.
VOYAGE OF APPROXIMATELY 4100 MILES AT 20.0 KTS.
VESSEL MUST MAINTAIN 2% OF 76 FT. BEAM OR 1.5 FT. GM THROUGHOUT
VOYAGE (AFTER ALL CORRECTIONS).

LOAD DISPLACEMENT	21094T.
LIGHT SHIP	7675T.
DEADWEIGHT	13419T.
CONSUMABLES	1050T.
CARGO	12369T.

56T.   82IT.   847T.   II9T.   II8T.   6IIT.   32T.

8% FEEDER   8% FEEDER   8% FEEDER   8% FEEDER   8% FEEDER   8% FEEDER   8% FEEDER   5% FEEDER

70IT.   I296T.   305T. 306T.   781T.   II6IT. I207T.   II36T. I023T.   693T. 5I7T.   369T. 270T.

DEPARTURE DATA

CONSUMABLES:
CREW, STORES, FITTINGS	150T.
FRESH WATER (BLUE)	200T.
FUEL OIL (GREEN)	700T.
TOTAL	1050T.

STABILITY:
DEPARTURE (APPROX.) 1.7 FT. GM
ARRIVAL (APPROX.) 1.6 FT. GM
(MAINTAINED BY BALLASTING AS FUEL IS BURNED OFF.)

EST. MEAN SAILING DRAFT: 29'-10"

MARINER (C4-S-ld) TYPE

12369 TONS (561593 bu.) BARLEY 49.5 lb./bu.
STOWING AT 56.3 cu. ft./ton. REQUIRES 696375 cu. ft.

SPACE USED AS FOLLOWS:

LOWER HOLDS AND LOWER TWEEN DECKS		549785 cu. ft.	
FEEDERS:	No. 1	1796	5%
	No. 2	5452	8%
	No. 3	9725	8%
	No. 4	10666	8%
	No. 5	6270	8%
	No. 6	5834	8%
	No. 7	3157	8%
UPPER TWEEN DECKS:	No. 2	28100	
	No. 5	39670	
	No. 6	38593	
TWEEN DECK FEEDERS:	No. 2	833	
	No. 5	1740	
	No. 6	1813	
TOTAL:		703434 cu. ft.	

FEEDERS SLACK EXCEPT NO. 1
(ALL TO CONTAIN NOT LESS THAN
5%)

MARINER (C4-S-1d) TYPE

SUMMER DISPLACEMENT	21093T.
LIGHTSHIP	7675T.
DEADWEIGHT	13418T.
CONSUMABLES	1646T.
CARGO	11770T.

11770 TONS (664447 BUSHELS) OATS AT 70 CU. FT. PER TON.
VOYAGE OF APPROXIMATELY 6900 MILES AT 20.0 KTS.
MUST MAINTAIN 2% OF 76 FT. BEAM OR 1.5 FT. GM THROUGHOUT
VOYAGE (AFTER ALL CORRECTIONS).

Plan view cargo figures: 274T. 491T. 702T. 686T. 681T. 661T. 416T.

Profile figures: 217T. 296T. 557T. 416T. 914T. 823T. 934T. 975T. 246T. 246T. 628T. 1043T. 564T.

Feeder labels: 8% FEEDER, 5% FEEDER

STABILITY:
DEPARTURE (APPROX.) 1.8 FT. GM
ARRIVAL (APPROX.) 1.6 FT. GM
(MAINTAINED BY BALLASTING AS FUEL IS BURNED OFF.)

DEPARTURE DATA

CONSUMABLES:

CREW, STORES, FITTINGS	150T.
FRESH WATER (BLUE)	256T.
FUEL OIL (GREEN)	1240T.
TOTAL	1646T.

EST. MEAN SAILING DRAFT: 29'-10"

MARINER (C4-S-Id) TYPE

11770 TONS (664447 bu.) OATS AT 70 cu. ft./ton

SPACE USED AS FOLLOWS:

LOWER HOLDS:		326250 cu. ft.	
LOWER TWEEN DECKS:		223535	
TOTAL:		549785	
FEEDERS:	No. 1	1796	5%
	No. 2	5452	8%
	No. 3	9725	8%
	No. 4	10666	8%
	No. 5	6270	8%
	No. 6	5834	8%
	No. 7	3157	8%
TOTAL:		42900	
UPPER TWEEN DECKS:	No. 1	17266	
	No. 2	28100	
	No. 3	38234	
	No. 4	36369	
	No. 5	39670	
	No. 6	38593	
	No. 7	24818	
TOTAL:		223050	
TWEEN DECK FEEDERS:	No. 1	423	2.5%
	No. 2	833	3.6%
	No. 3	1196	3.1%
	No. 4	1015	2.8%
	No. 5	1740	4.4%
	No. 6	1813	4.5%
	No. 7	1160	4.5%
TOTAL:		8180	
GRAND TOTAL:		823915 cu. ft.	

103

NATIONAL CARGO BUREAU, INC.

S.S./M.V.	
PORT OF REGISTRY	OFFICIAL No.
AGENTS	

STABILITY CALCULATIONS

FOR

GENERAL CARGO VESSELS
LOADED WITH BULK GRAIN
CARGO IN ACCORDANCE WITH
CHAPTER VI, SOLAS 1960
OR SUBPART M, PART 144
U.S.C.G. REGULATIONS.

_____ __ _____

Loading Port_____

Discharge Port_____

Steaming Distance_____Time_____

Consumption: Fuel_____Water_____

Bunkering Port_____

_____ __ _____

THIS IS TO CERTIFY THAT THE CALCULATIONS AS SHOWN IN THIS
DOCUMENT INDICATE THE MINIMUM METACENTRIC HEIGHT WHICH
WILL BE MAINTAINED FOR THIS VESSEL THROUGHOUT THE VOYAGE.

_____
Master

EXAMINED:_____
N.C.B. Surveyor

DATE:_____

NOTE: *Stability Calculations and grain arrangement plan to be submitted in duplicate to the N.C.B. Surveyor.*
All tonnages used in these calculations are to be in LONG TONS.

REV. 7-62

Ship and Cargo Calculations

	WEIGHT (TONS)	V.C.G.	MOMENT
LIGHT SHIP			
Cargo			
Ship and Cargo Totals			

Feeders

Breadth _____ ft.

Total Length _____ ft.

Type of Grain_____

Stowage Factor (SF)_____cu. ft./ton

Loss of GM due to grain free surface in feeders without C/L divisions:
(Applies only under 46 CFR 144.20-10 (b) (2))

$$\frac{\text{feeder length} \times (\text{breadth})^3}{5 \times SF \times W}$$

Loss of GM due to free surface of liquids:

$$= \frac{\text{Sum of free surface inertia moment column}}{W}$$

i = Inertia Moment of free surface in individual slack tank (ft. tons)

$$= \frac{\text{Length} \times (\text{breadth})^3}{12 \times \delta}$$

δ = Density of liquid in tank (In cu. ft./ton)

W = Displacement tonnage

(For rectangular tanks only. For irregularly shaped tanks and for 98% full fuel oil tanks, free surface inertia moment data from valid source such as vessels trim and stability booklet shall be used.)

106

Fuel and Water Calculations

NOTE: Section 2 shall be filled out if Section 3 indicates carriage of salt water ballast. Section 2 shall represent the stage of the voyage just prior to taking salt water ballast aboard and the corrected GM shall be sufficient to meet minimum GM required.

TANK	SECTION 1				SECTION 2				SECTION 3			
	DEPARTURE			FREE SURFACE INERTIA MOMENT	INTERMEDIATE			FREE SURFACE INERTIA MOMENT	ARRIVAL			FREE SURFACE INERTIA MOMENT
	WEIGHT (TONS)	V.C.G.	MOMENT		WEIGHT (TONS)	V.C.G.	MOMENT		WEIGHT (TONS)	V.C.G.	MOMENT	

Totals
Liquids_____   _____   *_____ _____   _____   **_____ _____   _____   ***_____
Ship and Cargo _____   _____   _____ _____   _____ _____
Grand Totals (W)_____   _____   (W)_____   (W)_____   _____
Departure KG_____   Intermediate KG_____   Arrival KG_____   _____
Free Surface Corr.   Free Surface Corr.   Free Surface Corr.

Departure KM   Intermediate KM   Arrival KM
"   KG_____   "   KG_____   "   KG_____

Feeder Corr. (—)   Feeder Corr. (—)   Feeder Corr. (—)
Liquids F.S. Corr. (—) Liquids F.S. Corr. (—) Liquids F.S. Corr. (—)
Departure GM_____ Intermediate GM_____ Arrival GM_____

* Do not use total less than_____
** Do not use total less than_____
*** Do not use total less than_____   See 46 CFR 144.20-34(a)(3)

USEFUL INFORMATION
Metric Conversions

Millimeters	X .03937	= Inches
Millimeters	÷ 25.4	= Inches
Centimeters	X .3937	= Inches
Centimeters	÷ 2.54	= Inches
Meters	X 39.37	= Inches
Meters	X 3.28	= Feet
Meters	X 1.094	= Yards
Sq. Millimeters	X .00155	= Square Inches
Sq. Millimeters	÷ 645	= Square Inches
Sq. Centimeters	X .155	= Square Inches
Sq. Centimeters	÷ 6.45	= Square Inches
Sq. Meters	X 10.764	= Square Feet
Cubic Centimeters	÷ 16.387	= Cubic Inches
Cubic Meters	X 35.314	= Cubic Feet
Cubic Meters	X 1.308	= Cubic Yards
Cubic Meters	X 264.2	= Gallons (231 Cubic Inches)
Kilograms	X 2.2046	= Pounds
Kilograms	X 35.27	= Ounces Avoirdupois
Kilograms	÷ 907.18	= Short Tons (2000 pounds)
Kilograms per Square Centimeter	X 14.223	= Pounds per Square Inch
Kilograms per Cubic Meter	X .062	= Pounds per Cubic Foot
Cubic Feet	X 1728	= Cubic Inches
Cubic Feet	X 7.481	= Gallons
Cubic Feet (Fresh Water)	X 62.5	= Pounds of Fresh Water
Cubic Feet (Sea Water)	X 64.0	= Pounds of Sea Water
Feet	X 30.48	= Centimeters
Feet	X .3048	= Meters
Gallons	X 231	= Cubic Inches
Gallons	X 8.33	= Pounds of Fresh Water
Inches	X 2.54	= Centimeters
Pounds	X .4536	= Kilograms
Tons (long) Fresh Water	X 35.9	= Cubic Feet of Fresh Water
Tons (long) Sea Water	X 35	= Cubic Feet of Sea Water

Temperature Scale Conversions

F = Fahrenheit $F = 9/5C + 32°$

C = Centigrade $C = (F - 32°) \times 5/9$

Board Measure

Number of Feet = Length in Feet X Width in Feet X Thickness in Inches

Approximate Equivalents

1 Meter	=	39.37	Inches
1 Kilogram	=	2.204	Pounds
1 Centimeter	=	.39	Inches
1 Metric Ton	= 2204		Pounds
1 Ton Fresh Water	= 269		U. S. Gallons

DISTANCES IN NAUTICAL MILES

STRAIT OF GIBRALTAR TO:	Miles
Alexandria	1823
Baltimore	3461
Boston	3031
Charleston	3593
Genoa	877
Haifa	2028
Istanbul	1819
Karachi	4800
Marseilles	712
Montreal	3243
Naples	999
New York	3211
Norfolk	3335
Panama	4351
Philadelphia	3344
Port Said	1935
Portland, Me.	3031
Quebec	3104
Rijeka	1665
Straits of Florida	4038
Trieste	1710

STRAITS OF FLORIDA
(24° 25′ N., 83° 00′ W.) TO:

	Miles
Baltimore	1115
Baton Rouge	656
Bishop Rock	3887
Bordeaux	4284
Boston	1440
Charleston	644
Corpus Christi	803
Dakar	3744
Galveston	698
Gulfport	494
Halifax	1642
Lisbon	3831
Mobile	471
New Orleans	524
New York	1197
Norfolk	997
Pensacola	431
Philadelphia	1168
Port Arthur	677
Portland, Me.	1485
Tampa	232

BISHOP ROCK TO:	Miles
Amsterdam	481
Antwerp	449
Baltimore	3290
Bergen	911
Boston	2860
Bremerhaven	657
Hamburg	717
London	413
Montreal	3055
New York	3019
Norfolk	3168
Philadelphia	3159
Portland, Me.	2891

PENTLAND FIRTH TO:	
Amsterdam	481
Antwerp	553
Baltimore	3520
Bergen	296
Boston	3090
Bremerhaven	507
Montreal	2641
(via Belle Isle St.)	
New York	3240
Norfolk	3399
Philadelphia	3393

MONTREAL TO:	
Bay City	724
Buffalo	336
Chicago	1080
Cleveland	456
Detroit	528
Duluth-Superior	1158
Erie	373
Hamilton	203
Milwaukee	1021
Muskegon	993
Port Colborne	316
Port Huron	583
Port Weller	293
Quebec	139
Sault Ste. Marie	817
Toledo	524
Toronto	203

PANAMA TO:

	Miles
Antofagasta	2140
Baltimore	1944
Bishop Rock	4388
Bordeaux	4641
Boston	2200
Callao	1350
Galveston	1536
Gulfport	1431
Honolulu	4685
Kobe	7964
Los Angeles	2913
Manila	9370
Montreal	3203
New Orleans	1444
New York	2018
Norfolk	1822
Pensacola	1412
Philadelphia	1989
Port Arthur	1528
Portland, Oregon	3869
San Francisco	3245
Seattle	4020
Valparaiso	2616
Yokohama	7682

HONOLULU TO:

Hong Kong	4857
Kobe	3669
Los Angeles	2228
Manila	4869
Portland, Ore.	2332
Pusan	3973
Saigon	5542
San Francisco	2091
Seattle	2409
Sydney	4420
Yokohama	3450

YOKOHAMA TO:

Kobe	357
Los Angeles	4840
Manila	1758
Portland, Ore.	4328
San Francisco	4536
Seattle	4276

PORT ARTHUR TO:

	Miles
Casablanca	4565
Hamburg	5353
Karachi	9508
Naples	5681
San Juan	1694

NEW ORLEANS TO:

London	4893
Maracaibo	1672
Naples	5528
Piraeus	6068
Rotterdam	4939
Yokohama	9115

SAN FRANCISCO TO:

Oran	7844
San Juan	4281
Yokohama	4536

SEATTLE TO:

Calcutta	8700
Piraeus	9896
Yokohama	4254

PORTLAND, ORE. TO:

Bombay	9583
Calcutta	8780
Yokohama	4323

DULUTH TO:

Barcelona	4926
Maracaibo	4157
Oran	4656
Port au Prince	3813
Rotterdam	4480

CHICAGO TO:

London	4350
Rotterdam	4396

GRAIN STOWAGE FACTORS

1 U.S. Bushel = 1.2445 Cu. Ft.

$$\frac{2240 \text{ lbs.}}{\text{Test Weight per bu. (lbs.)}} \times 1.2445 \text{ cu. ft.} = \text{cu. ft. per long ton}$$

TEST WEIGHT	CU. FT. PER LONG TON	TEST WEIGHT	CU. FT. PER LONG TON
32	87.11	50	55.75
33	84.47	51	54.66
34	81.99	52	53.61
35	79.65	53	52.60
36	77.43	54	51.62
37	75.34	55	50.68
38	73.36	56	49.78
39	71.48	57	48.91
40	69.69	58	48.06
41	67.99	59	47.25
42	66.37	60	46.46
43	64.83	61	45.70
44	63.35	62	44.96
45	61.95	63	44.25
46	60.60	64	43.56
47	59.31	65	42.89
48	58.08	66	42.24
49	56.89	67	41.61

CANADIAN IMPERIAL BUSHEL

1 Imperial Bushel = 1.2837 cu. ft.

2240 × 1.2837 cu. ft. = 2875.49 cu. ft.

2875.49 ÷ Test weight per bushel = actual cubic feet per long ton.

TEST WEIGHT	CU. FT. PER LONG TON	TEST WEIGHT	CU. FT. PER LONG TON
32	89.86	50	57.51
33	87.14	51	56.38
34	84.57	52	55.30
35	82.16	53	54.25
36	79.87	54	53.25
37	77.72	55	52.28
38	75.67	56	51.35
39	73.73	57	50.45
40	71.89	58	49.58
41	70.13	59	48.74
42	68.46	60	47.92
43	66.87	61	47.14
44	65.35	62	46.38
45	63.90	63	45.64
46	62.51	64	44.93
47	61.18	65	44.24
48	59.91	66	43.57
49	58.68	67	42.92

GRAIN STANDARDS OF THE UNITED STATES

WHEAT

Hard Red Spring Wheat

    #1 Heavy — 60 lbs. per bushel — 46.46 cubic feet per ton
    #1   58 lbs. per bushel — 48.06 cubic feet per ton
    #2   57 lbs. per bushel — 48.91 cubic feet per ton
    #3   55 lbs. per bushel — 50.68 cubic feet per ton
    #4   53 lbs. per bushel — 52.60 cubic feet per ton
    #5   50 lbs. per bushel — 55.75 cubic feet per ton

Durum Wheat

    #1   60 lbs. per bushel — 46.46 cubic feet per ton
    #2   58 lbs. per bushel — 48.06 cubic feet per ton
    #3   56 lbs. per bushel — 49.78 cubic feet per ton
    #4   54 lbs. per bushel — 51.62 cubic feet per ton
    #5   51 lbs. per bushel — 54.66 cubic feet per ton

Hard Red Winter Wheat

    #1   60 lbs. per bushel — 46.46 cubic feet per ton
    #2   58 lbs. per bushel — 48.06 cubic feet per ton
    #3   56 lbs. per bushel — 49.78 cubic feet per ton
    #4   54 lbs. per bushel — 51.62 cubic feet per ton
    #5   51 lbs. per bushel — 54.66 cubic feet per ton

Soft Red Winter Wheat

    #1   60 lbs. per bushel — 46.46 cubic feet per ton
    #2   58 lbs. per bushel — 48.06 cubic feet per ton
    #3   56 lbs. per bushel — 49.78 cubic feet per ton
    #4   54 lbs. per bushel — 51.62 cubic feet per ton
    #5   51 lbs. per bushel — 54.66 cubic feet per ton

White Wheat

    #1   60 lbs. per bushel — 46.46 cubic feet per ton
    #2   58 lbs. per bushel — 48.06 cubic feet per ton
    #3   56 lbs. per bushel — 49.78 cubic feet per ton
    #4   54 lbs. per bushel — 51.62 cubic feet per ton
    #5   51 lbs. per bushel — 54.66 cubic feet per ton

CORN

Yellow Corn, White Corn and Mixed Corn

    #1   56 lbs. per bushel — 49.78 cubic feet per ton
    #2   54 lbs. per bushel — 51.62 cubic feet per ton
    #3   52 lbs. per bushel — 53.61 cubic feet per ton
    #4   49 lbs. per bushel — 56.89 cubic feet per ton
    #5   46 lbs. per bushel — 60.60 cubic feet per ton

BARLEY

Barley
#1	47 lbs. per bushel — 59.31 cubic feet per ton
#2	45 lbs. per bushel — 61.95 cubic feet per ton
#3	43 lbs. per bushel — 64.83 cubic feet per ton
#4	40 lbs. per bushel — 69.69 cubic feet per ton
#5	36 lbs. per bushel — 77.43 cubic feet per ton

Malting Barley and Blue Malting Barley
#1	47 lbs. per bushel — 59.31 cubic feet per ton
#2	45 lbs. per bushel — 61.95 cubic feet per ton
#3	43 lbs. per bushel — 64.83 cubic feet per ton

Choice Malting Two Row Western Barley
May weigh 52 lbs. or more per full bushel — 53.61 cubic feet per ton or less.

Western Barley
#1 to #5 grades — Test weights for Western Barley not given by U. S. Department of Agriculture.

LINSEED - FLAXSEED

Linseed
#1	49 lbs. per bushel — 56.89 cubic feet per ton
#2	47 lbs. per bushel — 59.31 cubic feet per ton

SOYBEANS

Soybeans
#1	56 lbs. per bushel — 49.78 cubic feet per ton
#2	54 lbs. per bushel — 51.62 cubic feet per ton
#3	52 lbs. per bushel — 53.61 cubic feet per ton
#4	49 lbs. per bushel — 56.89 cubic feet per ton

GRAIN SORGHUMS

Grain Sorghums
#1	55 lbs. per bushel — 50.68 cubic feet per ton
#2	53 lbs. per bushel — 52.60 cubic feet per ton
#3	51 lbs. per bushel — 54.66 cubic feet per ton
#4	49 lbs. per bushel — 56.89 cubic feet per ton

RYE

Rye
#1	56 lbs. per bushel — 49.78 cubic feet per ton
#2	54 lbs. per bushel — 51.62 cubic feet per ton
#3	52 lbs. per bushel — 53.61 cubic feet per ton
#4	49 lbs. per bushel — 56.89 cubic feet per ton

SAFFLOWER SEED

Safflower Seed
40 to 42 lbs. per bushel — 69.69 to 66.37 cubic feet per ton

OATS
White Oats, Red Oats, Gray Oats, Black Oats and Mixed Oats

#1	34 lbs. per bushel —	81.99 cubic feet per ton
#2	32 lbs. per bushel —	87.11 cubic feet per ton
#3	30 lbs. per bushel —	92.72 cubic feet per ton
#4	27 lbs. per bushel —	103.30 cubic feet per ton

Heavy Oats
36 to 38 lbs. per bushel — 77.43 to 73.36 cubic feet per ton

Extra Heavy Oats
38 lbs. or more per bushel — 73.36 or less cubic feet per ton

NOTES:—

(1) *United States* bushel of 50 pounds or under per full bushel of 1.2445 cubic feet is used above.

(2) *Canadian* bushel : 51.575 pounds or under per full bushel of 1.2837 cubic feet.

(3) *Cubic feet per ton* are long tons of 2240 pounds.

(4) *Re: Grading Barley* — Some authorities divide barley into two (2) types, i.e., *Two row* and *Six row* barley. *Two row* has clusters of two (2) on each side of stalk. *Six row* has clusters of three (3) on each side of stalk. *The two row* is more stubby. *The six row* is thinner and has longer tails. *Six row* is lighter than *two row*.

WEIGHTS PER FULL BUSHEL AND STOWAGE FACTORS OF MISCELLANEOUS GRAINS

BUCKWHEAT
48 to 50 lbs. per bushel — 58.08 to 55.75 cubic feet per ton

RAPESEED
52 lbs. per bushel — 53.61 cubic feet per ton

MILO
55 to 58 lbs. per bushel — 50.68 to 48.06 cubic feet per ton

PEAS
60 to 64 lbs. per bushel — 46.46 to 43.56 cubic feet per ton

SUNFLOWER SEED
30 lbs. per bushel — 92.7 cubic feet per ton

RICE
62 to 64 lbs. per bushel — 44.96 to 43.56 cubic feet per ton

ANGLES OF REPOSE OF VARIOUS GRAINS

Wheat	23°	*Rye*	32°
Corn	21°	*Safflower Seed*	28°
Barley	45/48°	*Oats*	21°
Linseed-Flaxseed	21°	*Rice*	20°
Soybeans	22°		

NATIONAL CARGO BUREAU, INC.

List of Main Offices

Home Office — 99 John Street
New York 38, N. Y.
BEekman 3-6880

East Gulf Coast — 529 Hibernia Bank Bldg.
New Orleans, Louisiana
JAckson 2-8400

West Gulf Coast — Cotton Exchange Bldg.
Houston, Texas
CApital 7-8244

Pacific Coast — 233 Sansome Street
San Francisco, California
YUkon 2-0795

Great Lakes — Transit Shed #2, Butler Drive
Lake Calumet Harbor
Chicago, Illinois
MItchell 6-2131

Safety of Life at Sea Convention, 1948
Excerpt From CHAPTER VI — CARRIAGE OF GRAIN

Regulation 2
Carriage of Grain

(a) The term "grain" includes wheat, maize (corn), oats, rye, barley, rice, pulses, and seeds.

(b) Where grain is loaded in a ship, all necessary and reasonable precautions shall be taken to prevent the grain from shifting.

(c) Any compartment which is entirely filled with loose grain in bulk shall be:—

(i) fed by properly constructed feeders which shall contain not less than 2½ per cent. nor more than 8 per cent. of the capacity of the compartment served, and

(ii) divided by a longitudinal bulkhead or shifting boards, which shall be properly secured and fitted grain tight with proper fillers (fillings) between the beams. In holds such shifting boards shall extend downwards from the underside of the deck to a distance of at least one-third of the depth of the hold or 8 feet, whichever is the greater. In 'tween deck compartments they shall extend from deck to deck. In all cases they shall extend to the top of the feeders of the hold or compartment in which they are situated.

(d) In any compartment which is partially filled with loose grain in bulk, the grain shall be levelled and topped off with bagged grain or other suitable cargo extending to a height of not less than 4 feet above the top of the loose grain in bulk and supported on suitable platforms laid over the whole surface of the loose grain in bulk. In addition, the compartment shall be divided by a longitudinal bulkhead or shifting boards in line with the keel which shall extend from the bottom of the hold or deck as the case may be to a height sufficient to prevent the shifting of the loose grain in bulk. The fitting of a longitudinal bulkhead or shifting boards shall not be required if the grain in bulk does not exceed one-third the capacity of the compartment or, in the case of a compartment divided by a shaft tunnel, one-half the capacity of that compartment.

(e) Loose grain in bulk other than oats, light barley, and cotton seed shall not be carried in the 'tween decks of a two-deck ship, or in the uppermost 'tween decks of ships having more than two decks, except in properly constructed feeders as necessary for feeding the lower compartments. Loose grain in bulk may be carried in positions not otherwise permitted under this Regulation provided that:—

(i) It is carried in one or more bins, which shall be properly constructed and provided with feeders in accordance with the provisions of paragraph (c)(i).

(ii) The hold or compartment below the bin or bins is properly battened down, clear of the feeder to such hold or compartment.

(iii) The quantity of grain so carried does not exceed the capacity fixed by the Administration.

(f) Each Administration may, if it considers that the sheltered nature and conditions of the voyage are such as to render the application of any of the requirements of paragraphs (c) and (d) of this Regulation unreasonable or unnecessary, exempt from those particular requirements individual ships or classes of ships.

The International Convention for the Safety of Life at Sea—1960

CHAPTER VI.—CARRIAGE OF GRAIN

Regulation 1

Application

Unless expressly provided otherwise, this Chapter applies to the carriage of grain in all ships to which the present Regulations apply.

Regulation 2

Definition

The term "grain" includes wheat, maize (corn), oats, rye, barley, rice, pulses and seeds.

Regulation 3

Trimming

Where grain is loaded in a ship, all necessary and reasonable precautions shall be taken to prevent the grain from shifting. If any hold or compartment is entirely filled with bulk grain, the grain shall be trimmed so as to fill all the spaces between the beams and in the wings and ends.

Regulation 4

Stowage of full holds and compartments

Subject to the provisions of Regulation 6 of this Chapter, if any hold or compartment is entirely filled with bulk grain it shall be divided either by a longitudinal bulkhead or shifting boards in line with, or not more than 5 per cent. of the moulded breadth of the ship from, the centre line or by longitudinal bulkheads or shifting boards off the centre line of the ship provided that the distance between them shall not exceed 60 per cent. of the moulded breadth of the ship and that in the latter case trimming hatches of suitable size shall be provided in the wings at longitudinal intervals of not more than 25 feet (or 7·62 metres) with end trimming hatches placed not more than 12 feet (or 3·66 metres) from transverse bulkheads. In every case the longitudinal bulkheads or shifting boards shall be properly constructed and fitted grain-tight with proper fillings between the beams. In holds such longitudinal bulkheads or shifting boards shall extend downwards from the underside of the deck to a distance of at least one-third of the depth of the hold or 8 feet (or 2·44 metres) whichever is the greater. In compartments in 'tween decks and superstructures they shall extend from deck to deck. In all cases the longitudinal bulkheads or shifting boards shall extend to the top of the feeders of the hold or compartment in which they are situated.

Provided that in the case of ships loaded with bulk grain other than linseed in which a metacentric height (after correction for the free surface effects of liquids in tanks) is maintained throughout the voyage of not less than 12 inches (or 0·31 metres) in the case of one or two deck ships and not less than 14 inches (or 0·36 metres) in the case of other ships, longitudinal bulkheads or shifting boards need not be fitted:—

(a) below and within 7 feet (or 2·13 metres) of a feeder, but only in way of a hatchway, if that feeder contains, or all the feeders collectively feeding a compartment contain, not less than 5 per cent. of the quantity of grain carried in the compartment which is fed;

(b) in feeders which meet the requirements of paragraph (a) of this Regulation and which have such dimensions that the free grain surface will remain within the feeders throughout the voyage after allowing for a sinkage of grain amounting to 2 per cent. of the volume of the compartment fed and a shift of the free grain surface to an angle of 12 degrees to the horizontal; in this case the possible effects of the above mentioned movement of the free grain surfaces within the feeders shall be taken into account in calculating the metacentric height given above;

(c) in way of the hatchway where the bulk grain beneath the hatchway is trimmed in the form of a saucer hard up to the deckhead beyond the hatchway and is topped off with bagged grain or other suitable bagged cargo extending to a height in the centre of the saucer of not less than 6 feet (or 1·83 metres) above the top of the bulk grain (measured below the deck line) ; the bagged grain or other suitable bagged cargo shall fill the hatchway and the saucer below and shall be stowed tightly against the deckhead, the longitudinal bulkheads, the hatchway beams and the hatchway side and end coamings.

Regulation 5

Stowage of partly filled holds and compartments

Subject to the provisions of Regulation 6 of this Chapter, if any hold or compartment is partly filled with bulk grain:—

(a) it shall be divided by a longitudinal bulkhead or shifting boards, in line with, or not more than 5 per cent. of the moulded breadth of the ship from, the centre line or by longitudinal bulkheads or shifting boards off the centre line of the ship provided that the distance between them shall not exceed 60 per cent. of the moulded breadth of the ship. In every case the longitudinal bulkheads or shifting boards shall be properly constructed and shall extend from the bottom of the hold or deck, as the case may be, to a height of not less than 2 feet (or 0·61 metres) above the surface of the bulk grain.

Provided that, except in the case of holds partly filled with linseed in bulk, longitudinal bulkheads or shifting boards need not be fitted in way of the hatchway in the case of ships in which a metacentric height (after correction for the free surface effects of liquids in tanks) is maintained throughout the voyage of not less than 12 inches (or 0·31 metres) in the case of one or two deck ships and not less than 14 inches (or 0·36 metres) in the case of other ships;

(b) the bulk grain shall be levelled and topped off with bagged grain or other suitable cargo tightly stowed and extending to a height of not less than 4 feet (or 1·22 metres) above the top of the bulk grain within spaces divided by such a longitudinal bulkhead or shifting boards, and not less than 5 feet (or 1·52 metres) within spaces not so divided. The bagged grain or other suitable cargo shall be supported on suitable platforms laid over the whole surface of the bulk grain; such platforms shall consist of bearers spaced not more than 4 feet (or 1·22 metres) apart and 1 inch (or 25 millimetres) boards laid thereon spaced not more than 4 inches (or 0·10 metres) apart or of strong separation cloths with adequate overlapping.

Regulation 6
Exceptions to the requirements for longitudinal bulkheads
The fitting of longitudinal bulkheads or shifting boards in accordance with the provisions of Regulations 4 and 5 of this Chapter shall not be required:—

(a) in a lower hold (which term also includes the lower part of the hold of a single-deck ship) if the bulk grain therein does not exceed one-third of the capacity of the hold, or where such lower hold is divided by a shaft tunnel, one-half the capacity of that lower hold;

(b) in any space in a 'tween deck or superstructure provided that the wings are tightly stowed with bagged grain or other suitable cargo to a breadth on each side of not less than 20 per cent. of the breadth of the ship in way thereof; and (*c*) in those parts of spaces where the maximum breadth of the deckhead within the said spaces does not exceed one-half of the moulded breadth of the ship.

Regulation 7
Feeders

(*a*) (i) Any hold or compartment which is entirely filled with bulk grain shall be fed by suitably placed and properly constructed feeders, except as otherwise provided in paragraph (*c*) of Regulation 4 and Regulations 8 and 12 of this Chapter so as to secure a free flow of grain from the feeder to all parts of that hold or compartment.

(ii) Each feeder shall contain not less than 2 per cent. of the quantity of grain carried in that part of the hold or compartment that it feeds except as otherwise provided for in paragraph (*a*) of Regulation 4 of this Chapter.

(*b*) When bulk grain is carried in deep tanks primarily constructed for the carriage of liquids to which paragraph (*c*) of Regulation 6 of this Chapter applies or that are divided by one or more permanent steel longitudinal divisions fitted grain-tight, feeders to the tanks may be omitted if the tanks and tank hatchways are completely filled and the hatch covers secured.

Regulation 8
Common Loading

For the purpose of Regulations 4 and 7 of this Chapter lower holds and 'tween deck spaces over them may be loaded as one compartment under the following conditions:—

(*a*) longitudinal bulkheads or shifting boards shall be fitted deck to deck in the 'tween deck of a ship having two decks; in all other cases the longitudinal bulkheads or shifting boards shall be fitted for the upper third of the total depth of the common spaces;

(*b*) in order to secure an adequate flow of grain all spaces shall comply with the requirements of Regulation 9 of this Chapter and openings shall be provided in the wings of the deck immediately below the uppermost deck forward and aft of the ends of the hatchways as necessary to provide in combination with the hatchways a maximum feeding distance of 8 feet (or 2·44 metres) measured in a fore and aft line.

Regulation 9
Trimming and bagging of end spaces

When the distance, measured in a fore and aft line, from any part of a hold or compartment to the nearest feeder exceeds 25 feet (or 7·62 metres) the bulk grain in the end spaces beyond 25 feet (or 7·62 metres) from the nearest feeder shall be levelled off at a depth of at least 6 feet (or 1·83 metres) below the deck, and the end spaces filled with bagged grain built up on a suitable platform as required in paragraph (b) of Regulation 5 of this Chapter.

Regulation 10

Bulk grain in 'tween decks and superstructures

Bulk grain shall not be carried above deck, in the 'tween deck of a two deck ship, or in the uppermost 'tween deck of a ship having more than two decks except under the following conditions :—

(a) the bulk grain or other cargo shall be stowed so as to ensure maximum stability: in all cases either a metacentric height (after correction for the free surface effects of liquids in tanks) shall be maintained throughout the voyage of not less than 12 inches (or 0·31 metres) in the case of one or two deck ships and 14 inches (or 0·36 metres) in the case of other ships or, alternatively, the aggregate quantity of bulk grain or other cargo carried above deck, in the 'tween deck spaces of a two deck ship or in the uppermost 'tween deck spaces of a ship having more than two decks shall not exceed 28 per cent. by weight of the total cargo below the 'tween deck where the master is satisfied that the ship will have adequate stability throughout the voyage; the limitation of 28 per cent. specified above shall not apply when the grain carried above deck or in the uppermost 'tween deck spaces is oats, barley or cotton seed;

(b) the deck area of any portion of the spaces referred to in this Regulation which contains bulk grain and which is only partly filled shall not exceed 1,000 square feet (or·93 square metres) ; and

(c) all spaces referred to in this Regulation in which bulk grain is stowed shall be subdivided by transverse bulkheads at intervals of not more than 100 feet (or 30·50 metres) ; when this distance is exceeded the excess space shall be entirely filled with bagged grain or other suitable cargo.

Regulation 11

Limitation on number of partly filled holds and compartments

Except in the case of ships in which a metacentric height (after correction for the free surface effects of liquids in tanks) is maintained throughout the voyage of not less than 12 inches (or

0·31 metres) in the case of one or two deck ships and not less than 14 inches (or 0·36 metres) in the case of other ships, not more than two holds or compartments shall be partly filled with bulk grain, except that other holds or compartments may be partly filled with bulk grain if they are filled up to the deckhead with bagged or other suitable cargo. For the purpose of this Regulation:—

(a) superimposed 'tween decks shall be regarded as separate compartments and separate from any lower hold below them;

(b) feeders and the partly filled spaces referred to in paragraph (b) of Regulation 10 of this Chapter shall not be regarded as compartments; and

(c) holds or compartments provided with one or more grain-tight longitudinal divisions shall be regarded as one hold or compartment.

Regulation 12
Stowage of specially suitable ships

(a) Notwithstanding anything contained in Regulations 4 to 11 of this Chapter, bulk grain may be carried without regard to the requirements specified therein in ships which are constructed with two or more vertical or sloping grain-tight longitudinal divisions suitably disposed to limit the effect of any transverse shift of grain under the following conditions:—

(i) as many holds and compartments as possible shall be full and trimmed full;

(ii) for any specified arrangement of stowage the ship will not list to an angle greater than 5 degrees at any stage of the voyage where:—

(1) in holds or compartments which have been trimmed full the grain surface settles 2 per cent. by volume from the original surface and shifts to an angle of 12 degrees with that surface under all boundaries of these holds and compartments which have an inclination of less than 30 degrees to the horizontal; and

(2) in partly filled holds or compartments free grain surfaces settle and shift as in sub-paragraph (ii) (1) of this paragraph or to such larger angle as may be deemed necessary by the Administration, or by a Contracting Government on behalf of the Administration, and grain surfaces if overstowed in accordance with Regulation 5 of this Chapter shift to an

angle of 8 degrees with the original levelled surfaces. For the purposes of sub-paragraph (ii) of this paragraph shifting boards if fitted will be considered to limit the transverse shift of the surface of the grain;

(iii) the master is provided with a grain loading plan covering the stowage arrangements to be adopted and a stability booklet, both approved by the Administration, or by a Contracting Government on behalf of the Administration, showing the stability conditions upon which the calculations given in sub-paragraph (ii) of this paragraph are based.

(b) The Administration, or a Contracting Government on behalf of the Administration, shall prescribe the precautions to be taken against shifting in all other conditions of loading of ships designed in accordance with paragraph (a) of this Regulation which meet the requirements of sub-paragraphs (ii) and (iii) of that paragraph.

(c) The Administration, or a Contracting Government on behalf of the Administration, shall prescribe the precautions to be taken against shifting in a ship of any other design which meets the requirements of sub-paragraphs (ii) and (iii) of paragraph (a) of this Regulation.

Regulation 13
Water ballast tanks
Double bottom tanks which are used to meet a stability requirement in ships loading bulk grain shall have adequate watertight longitudinal subdivision except where the width of the tank measured at half length does not exceed 60 per cent. of the ship's moulded breadth.

Regulation 14
Bagged grain
Bagged grain shall be carried in sound bags which shall be well filled and securely closed.

Regulation 15
Grain loading plans
(a) A grain loading plan approved for a ship whether by the Administration or by a Contracting Government on behalf of the Administration shall be accepted by other Contracting Governments as evidence that the ship when loaded in accordance with such plans meets the requirements of this Chapter or equivalent arrangements which have been accepted under Regulation 5 of Chapter I.

(*b*) Such plan shall be approved after taking into account the requirements of this Chapter, the various circumstances of loading on departure and arrival, and the stability of the ship. It shall indicate the main characteristics of the fittings used to prevent the shifting of cargo.

(*c*) Such plan shall be annotated in one or more languages of which one shall be one of the Convention languages.

(*d*) A copy of such plan shall be supplied to the master of the ship, who if so required shall produce it for the inspection of the appropriate authority of the port in which loading takes place.

(*e*) Pending the adoption of international regulations concerning the strength of grain fittings and the provision of feeding holes in hatch coamings, a ship loading grain which does not produce a grain loading plan approved by the Administration, or by a Contracting Government on behalf of the Administration, shall load in accordance with detailed rules issued to supplement the provisions of this Chapter by the Contracting Government of the country in which the loading port is situated.

Regulation 16
Exemptions for certain voyages
The Administration, or a Contracting Government on behalf of the Administration, may, if it considers that the sheltered nature and conditions of the voyage are such as to render the application of any of the requirements of Regulations 3 to 15 of this Chapter unreasonable or unnecessary, exempt from those particular requirements individual ships or classes of ships.